SOLUTIONS MANUAL TO ACCOMPANY

STATISTICAL ANALYSIS FOR DECISION MAKING

FIFTH EDITION

SOLUTIONS MANUAL TO ACCOMPANY

STATISTICAL ANALYSIS FOR DECISION MAKING

FIFTH EDITION

MORRIS HAMBURG
THE WHARTON SCHOOL
UNIVERSITY OF PENNSYLVANIA

HARCOURT BRACE JOVANOVICH, PUBLISHERS
AND ITS SUBSIDIARY, *ACADEMIC PRESS*
SAN DIEGO NEW YORK CHICAGO AUSTIN WASHINGTON, D.C.
LONDON SYDNEY TOKYO TORONTO

ISBN: 0-15-583463-0

Printed in the United States of America

Preface

The answers in this Solutions Manual have been carefully checked for accuracy. Any residual errors in this Manual or in the textbook should be brought to the attention of the author.

Contents

CHAPTER 1

Exercises 1.6

1. a. Using five classes we have the following table for audiences at Expo-Classic:

	Frequency
600 and under 900	2
900 and under 1,200	11
1,200 and under 1,500	8
1,500 and under 1,800	6
1,800 and under 2,100	3
Total	30

   b. The frequency polygon and frequency curve, respectively, for audience sizes appear as follows:

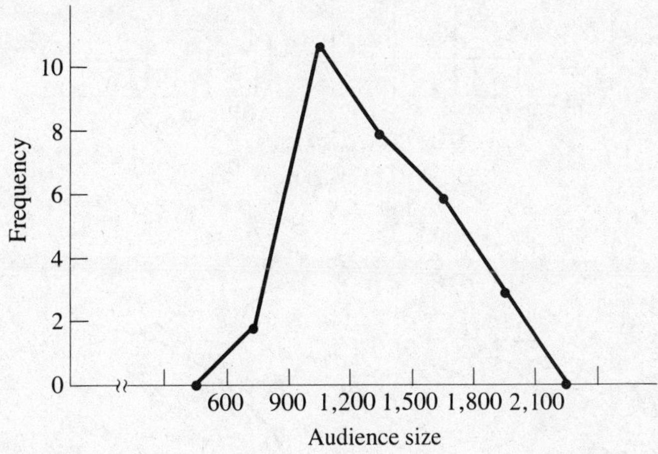

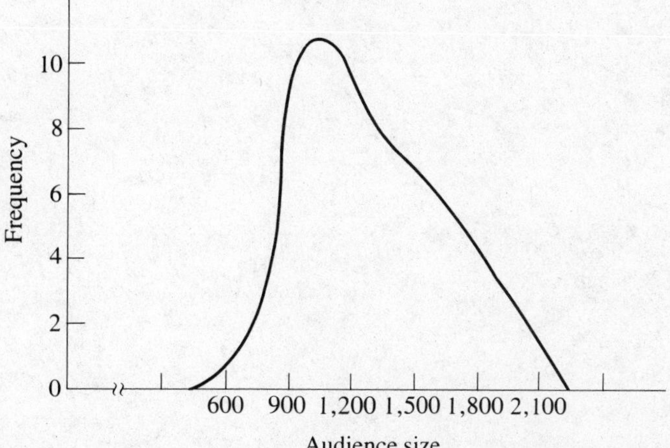

2. a. Using seven classes, we have the following distribution for donations received at Union-Path offices:

Donations (thousands of dollars)	Midpoints	Frequency
20.0 and under 55.0	37.5	1
55.0 and under 90.0	72.5	3
90.0 and under 125.0	107.5	6
125.0 and under 160.0	142.5	8
160.0 and under 195.0	177.5	4
195.0 and under 230.0	212.5	2
230.0 and under 265.0	247.5	1
Total		25

b. That distribution yields the following histogram and "less than" ogive, respectively.

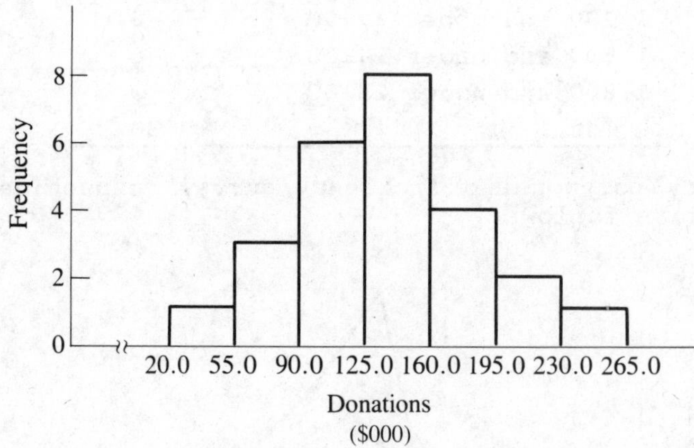

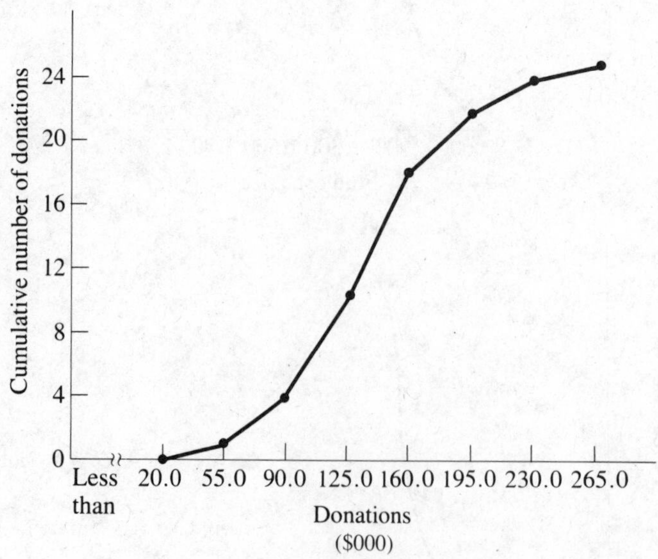

3. The cumulative frequency distribution is as follows:

Policy Size	Number of Ordinary Life Insurance Policies in Force per 1,000 Policies
Less than $1,000	31
Less than $2,500	212
Less than $5,000	320
Less than $10,000	533
Less than maximum	1,000

4. a. The class intervals are not mutually exclusive; the class limits are unclear and overlapping.
   b. There is a gap in values between classes; thus, the classes are not exhaustive.

5. a. Using six classes, we have the following frequency distribution for worker-days lost last year at Ultra Corporation:

Worker-days Lost	Total	Frequency Midwest	South
75.0 and under 105.0	9	8	1
105.0 and under 135.0	10	6	4
135.0 and under 165.0	8	3	5
165.0 and under 195.0	5	1	4
195.0 and under 225.0	3	1	2
225.0 and under 255.0	1	1	0
Total	36	20	16

   b.

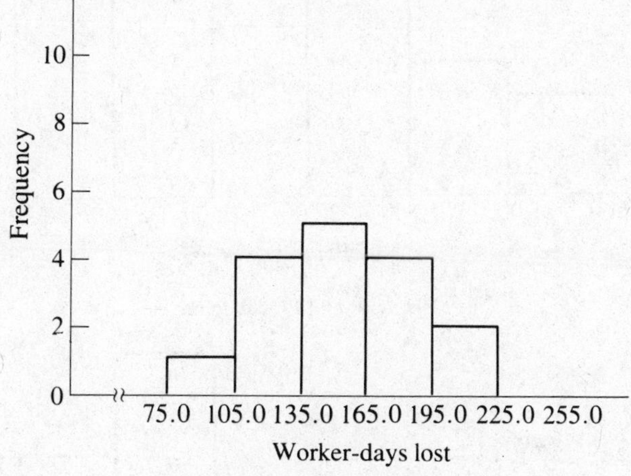

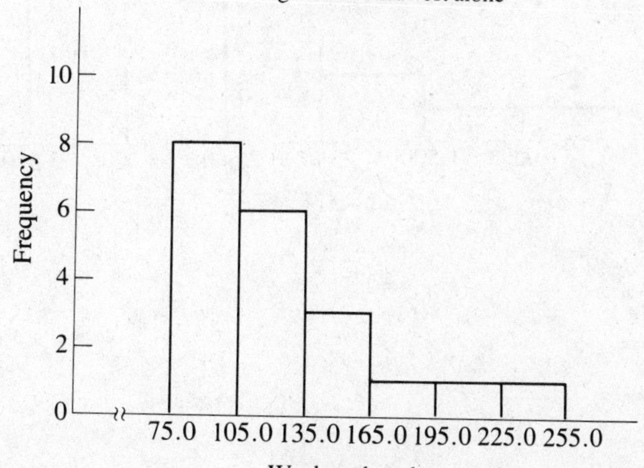

c. The South appears to have the bigger problem, because more of the area under its histogram is toward the right than for the Midwest. The histogram for the Midwest is concentrated toward the left.

From part a we get an overall picture. Part b shows us the differences between the regions and how those differences affect the overall distribution.

6. a and b. Number of boxes sold during the one-week period:

Number of Boxes	Total	Number of Stores Philadelphia	Camden
500 and under 1,000	3	1	2
1,000 and under 1,500	4	1	3
1,500 and under 2,000	8	2	6
2,000 and under 2,500	5	3	2
2,500 and under 3,000	10	9	1
3,000 and under 3,500	6	6	0
Total	36	22	14

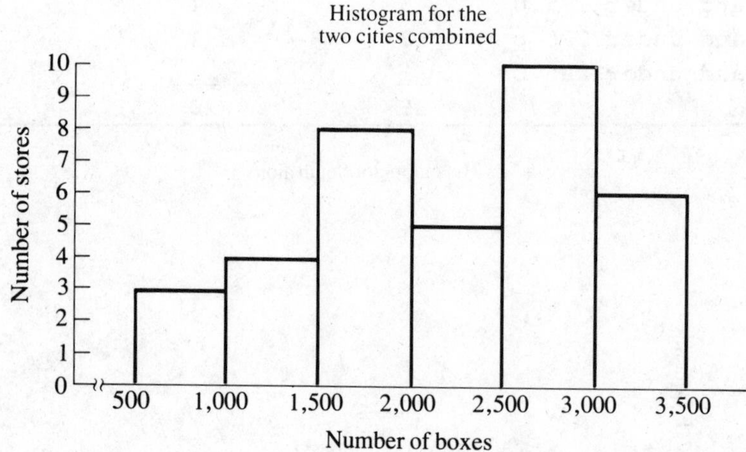

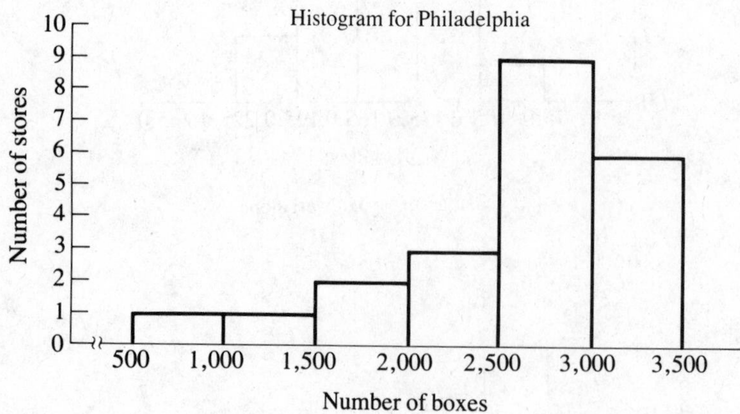

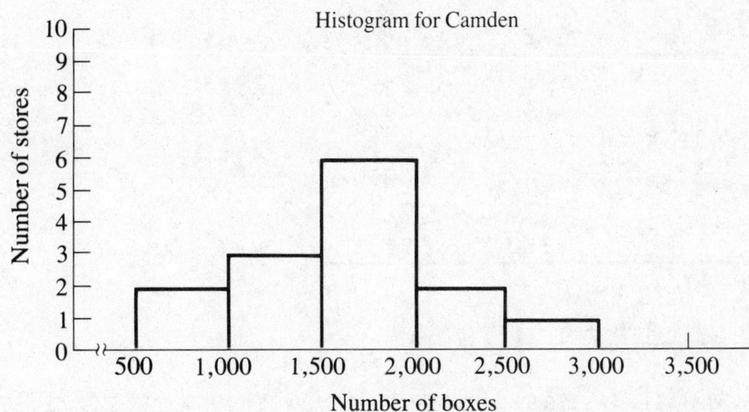

c. The answer in part b is preferable, because a bimodal distribution results if the data for the two market cities are merged.

7. a. Frequency table for credit positions of corporate clients:

Credit Outstanding (in millions of dollars)	Number of Companies	Midpoint (in millions of dollars)
0 and under 5	2	2.5
5 and under 10	4	7.5
10 and under 15	6	12.5
15 and under 20	5	17.5
20 and under 25	3	22.5
25 and under 30	4	27.5
30 and under 35	1	32.5

b.

Credit Outstanding	Number of Companies
Less than 5	2
Less than 10	6
Less than 15	12
Less than 20	17
Less than 25	20
Less than 30	24
Less than 35	25

Exercises 1.9

1. No. For example, suppose 99% of Center City's total dollar credit extended consists of personal loans and 99% of Neighborhood Bank's business is industrial loans. Then the overall debt ratios are

Center City = (0.99)(0.04) + (0.01)(0.02) = 0.0398
Neighborhood = (0.01)(0.05) + (0.99)(0.03) = 0.0302

2. a.

x	f	fx
2.5%	34	85%
7.5	46	345
12.5	38	475
17.5	22	385
22.5	10	225
	150	1515%

$$\overline{X} = \frac{1515\%}{150} = 10.1\%$$

3. a. $\dfrac{(3.6 + 3.8 + 2.5 + 6.5)}{4} = 4.1\%$

   b. $\overline{X}_w = (4118 + 8161 + 5158 + 54{,}805)/1{,}378{,}637 = 72{,}242/1{,}378{,}637 = 5.2\%$

   c. In the weighted average of part (b), the greatest weight is applied to the highest percentage unemployed, 6.5% (for County D). This pulls the weighted mean above the unweighted mean of part (a).

4. No, this is not enough information for us to make a decision. Because we do not know the proportions of the ingredients in the two spreads, we cannot say that Brandex has a lower *overall* Oxy-toxin content. For example, if the proportions are as follows, we could conclude that Brandex actually has a higher Oxy-toxin level:

	Proportion		Weighted Oxy-toxin Level (%)	
Ingredient	Brandex	Leading Spread	Brandex	Leading Spread
Moonflower oil	0.4	0.1	0.48	0.18
Processed butter-glop	0.3	0.4	0.18	0.32
Flavoring	0.1	0.4	0.03	0.12
Coloring	0.2	0.1	0.10	0.06
Total	1.0	1.0	0.79	0.68

From this table, we see an overall level of 0.79% for Brandex compared with an overall level of 0.68% for the leading spread. Therefore, we need to know the proportions of ingredients before we can make a decision. We also need to know about any ingredients that have not been advertised and the levels of Oxy-toxin in those ingredients as well.

5. a. The overall percentage of defectives for the last 50 runs is

$$\overline{X} = [(0.25)(3) + (0.75)(12) + (1.25)(24) + (1.75)(9) + (2.25)(2)]/50 = 1.2\%$$

   b. This method would not necessarily give the same answer, because the answer in part a is computed from a grouped data table using class midpoints, whereas the other is a mean computed from raw data.

6. a. Weighted average of pollutant level in the three tanks is

$$\overline{X} = \frac{(4.5)(261{,}432) + (15.0)(118{,}300) + (21.3)(287{,}456)}{667{,}188}$$

$= 13.6$ parts per 10,000

   b. Unweighted average is

$$\overline{X} = \frac{4.5 + 15.0 + 21.3}{3} = 13.6 \text{ parts per } 10{,}000$$

   c. Yes, the answer in part b shows an unexpected correspondence to that in part a.

7. a. For the first strategy, average cost of United Aerodynamics is (\$5,275/125) = \$42.20; average cost of Mitton Industries is (\$4,675/125) = \$37.40.

   For the second strategy, aveage cost of United Aerodynamics is (\$5,039/125) = \$40.31; average cost of Mitton Industries is (\$4,959/141) = \$35.17.

   b. The second strategy achieved the lower average cost for both stocks.

   c. For the second strategy, since the number of shares bought each time varied inversely with the stock price, higher weights were placed on the lower stock prices in the calculation of the average cost per share. This resulted in a lower overall average for each stock than in the first strategy, in which the average cost per share was the unweighted mean of the 5 share prices. That is, if equal weights are used in computing a weighted arithmetic mean, the resulting figure is the same as the unweighted mean.

Exercises 1.12

1. $$\bar{X} = \left(\frac{\$30 + \$45 + \cdots + \$41 + \$21}{30}\right) = \$38.97$$

   To find the median we have to rank the data:

\$15	\$30	\$33	\$41	\$46	\$49
21	30	33	42	47	50
26	30	39	45	48	51
28	32	40	45	48	51
29	33	41	45	49	52

   Since we have 30 values, the median is between the fifteenth and sixteenth entries.

   $$Md = \left(\frac{\$41 + \$41}{2}\right) = \$41$$

   Three values occur with equal frequency—30, 33, and 45. Thus, there is no unique mode.

2. Agree, since in all three cases it is quite logical to assume that there would be extreme values at the upper end of the scale and that such values would tend to make the arithmetic mean larger than the median.

3. a. Because the large account balances at the upper end of the distribution would make it impractical to have enough closed classes to encompass all account balances.

   b. Modal class: \$2000 to \$2499

   c. Median class: \$1500 to \$1999

4. a.

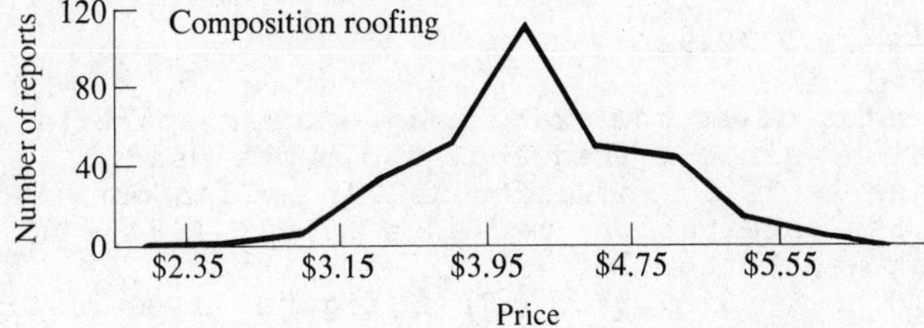

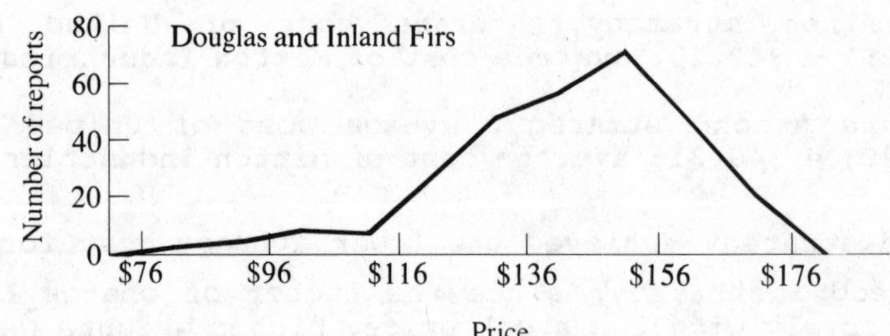

b. Composition roofing: Median class is $3.95 and under $4.35; modal class is $3.95 and under $4.35. Douglas and Inland Firs: Median class is $136-$145; modal class is $146-$155.

c.

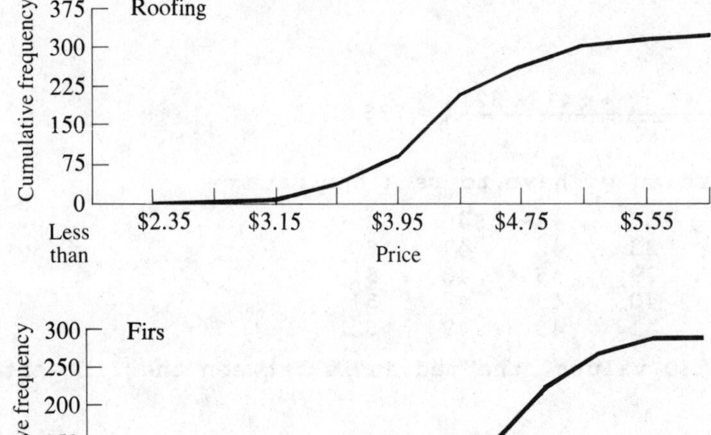

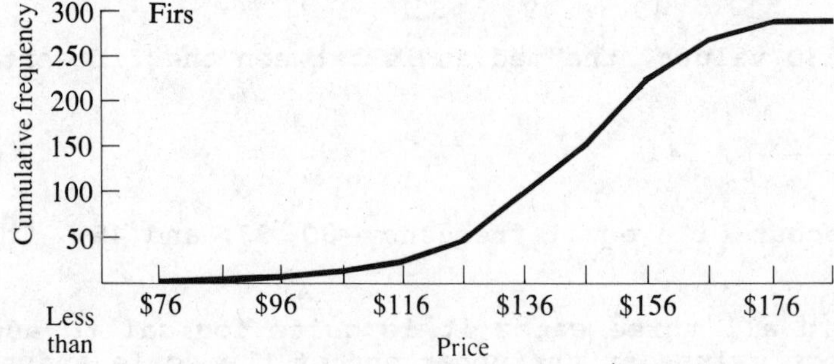

d. The distribution of composition roofing prices is nearly symmetrical, and the distribution of fir prices is skewed to the left.

5. a. A bi-modal frequency distribution indicates that more than one population is represented by the data. Hence, all measures of central tendency are misleading.

6. a. $\overline{X} = \dfrac{\$129{,}850}{168} = \$772.92$

b. No. This ratio gives the exact mean, whereas part (a) gives only a close approximation, since a frequency table was used.
c. Median class is "$750 and under $800"; median observation is the (168 + 1)/2 = 84.5th observation; median = $750 + [(84 - 66)/36]($50) = $775.
d. Slightly skewed to the left.
e. No, since Σfx is $129,850. This figure is an *estimate* of the total payroll and is close to the true figure of $129,832.
f. Yes, the mean here seems typical, since there is little skewness to distort it.

Exercises 1.13

1. $1 + r = \sqrt[10]{\dfrac{1,255,100}{845,600}}$

   $r = .040 = 4.0\%$ increase per year.

2. a. $1 + r = \sqrt[6]{\dfrac{2,000,000}{4,000,000}}$

   $r = -.1092 = -10.92\%$ per yr.

3. a. $\dfrac{\$25,000 - \$20,000}{5} = \$1,000$

   b. $1 + r = \sqrt[5]{\dfrac{\$25,000}{\$20,000}}$

   $r = .046 = 4.6\%$

   c. No. This average is not typical because of the widely differing five year rates of change.

4. a. $(\$4000)(1.09)^n = \$8000$

   $n = \dfrac{.3010}{.0374} = 8.05$

   Hence rounding off to the nearest whole number of years above 8.05, we find that 9 years are required.

   b. $(\$4,000)(1.09)^{4.5}$

   antilog 3.7704 = \$5,890

   c. $(\$4,000)(1.09)^{18}$

   antilog 4.2753 = \$18,850

   Compound interest has an exponential growth pattern. As the base becomes larger, the increase becomes greater.

Exercises 1.18

1. a. Both stocks have mean and median prices of \$25. Thus, there is no difference simply on the basis of measures of central tendency.

   b. s (Highfly) $= \sqrt{164/4} = \$6.40$

   s (Stabil) $= \sqrt{20/4} = \$2.24$

   The standard deviation is a measure of price fluctuation. Hence, it can be considered a measure of the risk associated with the stock.

2. a. Tiny Tot: arithmetic mean = $\bar{X}$ = \$1.10; standard deviation = $s = \sqrt{1.22/(10-1)}$ = \$0.37. Gigantic Game: arithmetic mean = $\bar{X}$ = \$7.80; standard deviation = s = $\sqrt{6.28/(10-1)}$ = \$0.84. Gigantic Game Corporation earnings per share showed greater absolute variation.

   b. Tiny Tot: coefficient of variation = $s/\bar{X}$ = \$0.37/\$1.10 = 33.6%. Gigantic Game: coefficient of variation = $s/\bar{X}$ = \$0.84/\$7.80 = 10.77%. Tiny Tot earnings per share showed relatively greater variation than Gigantic Game, according to the coefficient of variation.

3. a. $\bar{X} = 15$; Median = 15

   b. $\bar{X} = \dfrac{(9)(12) + (9)(17) + (3)(22) + (3)(27)}{24} = 17$

   Mean production on the other days is greater than mean production on Mondays.

c. CV Monday $= \frac{3.85}{15} = 25.7\%$

CV Other $= \frac{5.11}{17} = 30.1\%$

No. Other days have greater relative dispersion in production than do Mondays.

4. a. $\bar{X} = \frac{165}{5} = 33$ years

$s = \sqrt{\frac{974}{4}} = 15.6$ years

b. If a constant c is added to or subtracted from all items in a distribution, the mean is increased or decreased by that constant c. If a constant c is added to or subtracted from all items in a distribution, the standard deviation is unchanged.

5. <u>Standard scores</u>

$$z_a = \frac{x_a - \mu_a}{\sigma_a} = \frac{84 - 80}{4} = 1$$

$$z_b = \frac{x_b - \mu_b}{\sigma_b} = \frac{70 - 60}{7} = 1.43$$

The applicant's score on test B was relatively farther above the mean than his/her score on test A.

CHAPTER 2

Exercises 2.1

1. {(0111), (1011), (1101), (1110), (1111)}

2. 0 = fall
   1 = same
   2 = rise

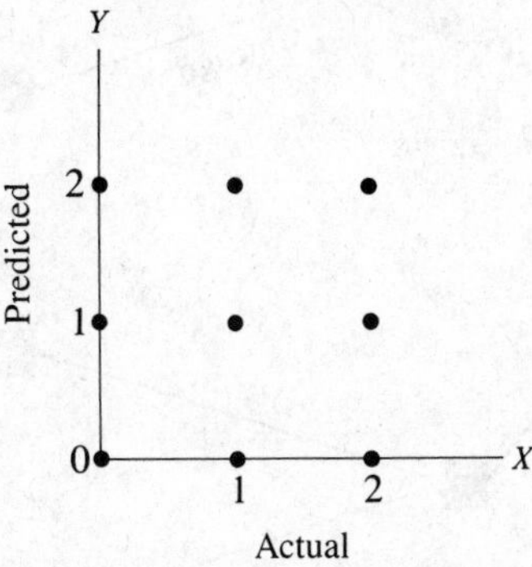

3. {A, RA, RRA, ... }

4. {(022), (202), (220), (122), (212), (221), (222)}

5. {(Los Angeles, Detroit, Philadelphia),
   (Los Angeles, Detroit, Baltimore),
   (Los Angeles, Detroit, Atlanta),
   (Los Angeles, Chicago, Philadelphia),
   (Los Angeles, Chicago, Baltimore),
   (Los Angeles, Chicago, Atlanta),
   (Seattle, Detroit, Philadelphia),
   (Seattle, Detroit, Baltimore),
   (Seattle, Detroit, Atlanta),
   (Seattle, Chicago, Philadelphia),
   (Seattle, Chicago, Baltimore),
   (Seattle, Chicago, Atlanta),}
   Total = 12 ways.

6.

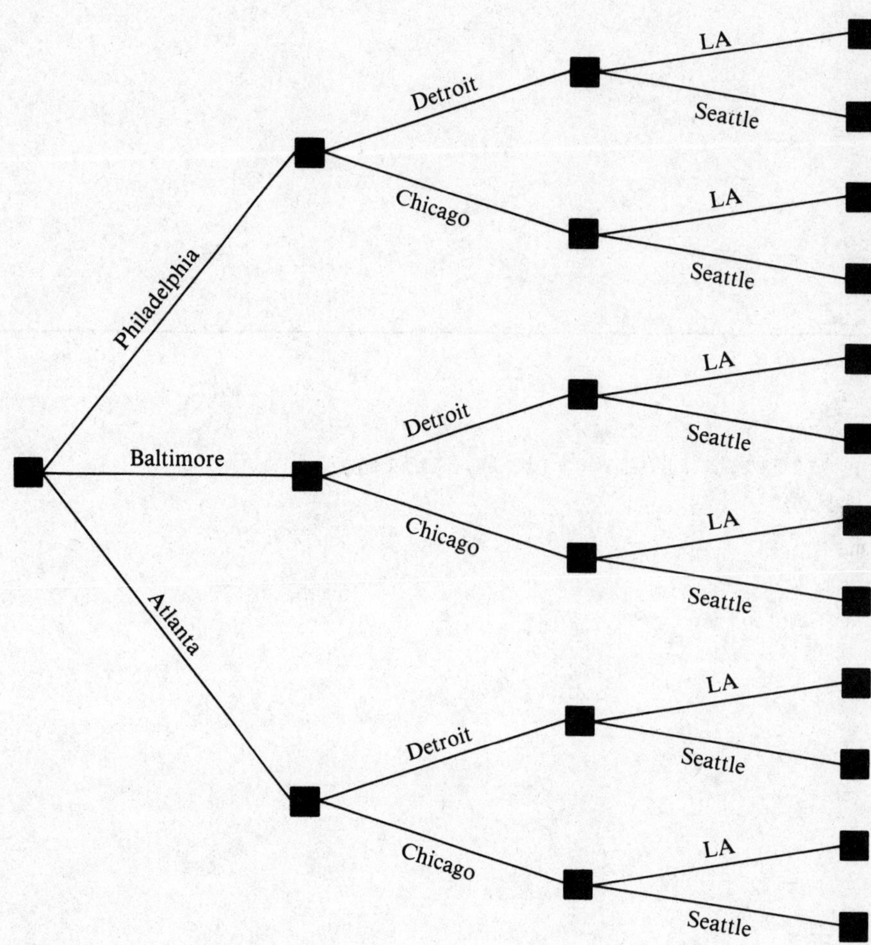

7.

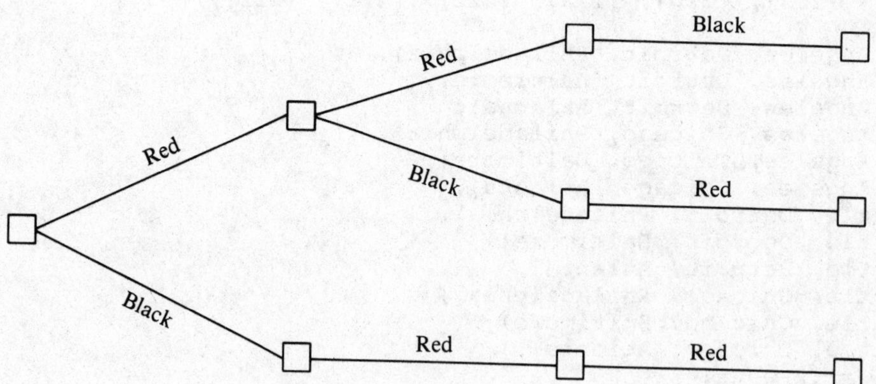

8. a. Yes
   b. Yes
   c. No
   d. Yes
   e. No

Exercises 2.2

1. a. No. P(bond prices fall and stock prices fall) $\neq 0$
   b. No. P(bond prices fall and stock prices fall) $\neq P$(bond prices fall) $\times$ P(stock prices fall)

2. 1 - (0.02) - (0.04) = 0.94

3. (0.06) $\times$ (0.06) = 0.0036

4. P(meets quota) = 1 - P(does not meet quota)
   = 1 - 0.2 = 0.8
   odds = 4:1

5. a. 1/6
   b. 1/6 + 1/6 + 1/6 = 1/2
   c. 1/6 + 1/6 + 1/6 = 1/2

6. a. {(*SSS*), (*SSN*), (*SNS*), (*NSS*), (*SNN*), (*NSN*), (*NNS*), (*NNN*)}
   b. 1/8
   c. P(do not vote unanimously)
   = 1 - P(all vote to strike) - P(all vote to work)
   = 1 - (1/2 $\times$ 1/2 $\times$ 1/2) - (1/2 $\times$ 1/2 $\times$ 1/2) = 6/8

7. $(0.6)^5 = 0.078$
   No, it is not a reasonable assumption.

8. a. (0.8 $\times$ 0.6 $\times$ 0.5) = 0.24
   b. (0.2 $\times$ 0.4 $\times$ 0.5) = 0.04
   c. Assume statistical independence

9. a. $(0.2)^5 = 0.00032$
   b. $(0.8)^5 = 0.33$
   c. $(0.8)^5 + 5(0.8)^4(0.2) = 0.74$

10. a.

	Size		
Opinion	Large	Small	Subtotal
Favor	100	150	250
Not in favor	200	50	250
Totals	300	200	500

   b. 50/500 = 0.1
   c. 250/500 = 0.5
   d. 50/200 = 0.25
   e. P(large corporation and favors reform) $\neq P$(large corporation) $\times P$(favors reform)
   Therefore, size of corporation and opinion of tax reform are not statistically independent.

11. a. 0.35
   b. 0.225
   c. 20/60 = 1/3
   d. 5/45 = 1/9
   e. No. P(low income and under 35) $\neq P$(low income) $\times P$(under 35)

Exercises 2.3

1. $$\frac{(0.7)(0.9)}{(0.7)(0.9) + (0.3)(0.2)} = 0.91$$

2. $\dfrac{(0.75)(0.07)}{(0.75)(0.07) + (0.25)(0.04)} = 0.84$

3. $\dfrac{(0.10)(0.25)}{(0.30)(0.20) + (0.10)(0.25) + (0.60)(0.95)} = 0.04$

4. Let θ = state of nature
   X = sample indicates high demand

State of Nature θ	$P(\theta)$	$P(x\|\theta)$	Joint Probabilities	$P(\theta\|x)$
High	0.55	0.80	(0.55)(0.80) = 0.44	0.71
Average	0.25	0.60	(0.25)(0.60) = 0.15	0.24
Low	0.20	0.15	(0.20)(0.15) = 0.03	0.05
Total	1.00		= 0.62	1.00

Exercises 2.4

1. 10! = 3,628,800

2. a. $10^3 = 1,000$
   b. $(26)(10^2) = 2,600$
   c. $(36)^3 = 46,656$

3. a. Any combination of 4 of the 12 colors.
   b. $\binom{12}{4} = 495$
   c. $\binom{11}{3} = 165$
   d. $\dfrac{165}{495} = \dfrac{1}{3}$, or $\dfrac{4}{12} = \dfrac{1}{3}$
   e. $\dfrac{\binom{10}{4}}{\binom{12}{4}} = \dfrac{210}{495} = 0.424$

4. $4! = 4 \times 3 \times 2 \times 1 = 24$

5. $\binom{7}{3} = 35$

6. $\binom{8}{3}\binom{6}{3} = (56)(20) = 1120$
   a. $\binom{8}{6} = 28$
   b. $\binom{6}{6} = 1$

7. a. (7)(12) = 84
   b. (7)(12)(11) = 924

8. a. $\binom{5}{3} = 10$

b. $(5)(4)(3) = 60$

c. $\dfrac{(3)(2)(1)}{(5)(4)(3)} = \dfrac{6}{60} = \dfrac{1}{10}$, or $\dfrac{1}{\binom{5}{3}} = \dfrac{1}{10}$

9. $\binom{10}{3}(3!) = 720$ or $(10)(9)(8) = 720$

10. a. $\dfrac{\binom{8}{1}\binom{8}{6}}{\binom{16}{7}} = \dfrac{(8)(28)}{11,440} = \dfrac{224}{11,440} = 0.0196$

b. $\dfrac{\binom{8}{1}\binom{7}{5}}{\binom{15}{6}} = \dfrac{(8)(21)}{5005} = \dfrac{168}{5005} = 0.0336$

c. $\dfrac{\binom{8}{6}}{\binom{15}{6}} = \dfrac{28}{5005} = 0.0056$

d. $\dfrac{\binom{9}{1}\binom{9}{6}}{\binom{18}{7}} = \dfrac{(9)(84)}{31,824} = \dfrac{756}{31,824} = 0.0238$

CHAPTER 3

Exercises 3.1

1. a. Continuous c. Discrete
   b. Continuous d. Discrete

   Although (a) and (b) are conceptually continuous random variables, in actual use they are discrete, because of the limited accuracy of the measuring instruments.

2. a. $P(X = 1) = f(1) = \frac{1}{14}(1)^2 = \frac{1}{14}$

   $P(X = 2) = f(2) = \frac{1}{14}(2)^2 = \frac{4}{14}$

   $P(X = 3) = f(3) = \frac{1}{14}(3)^2 = \frac{9}{14}$

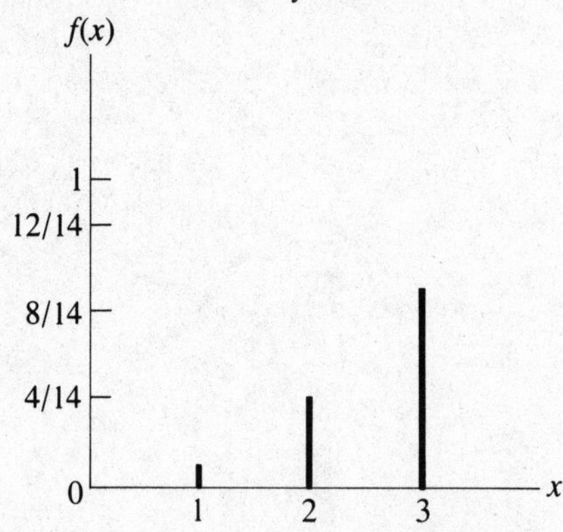

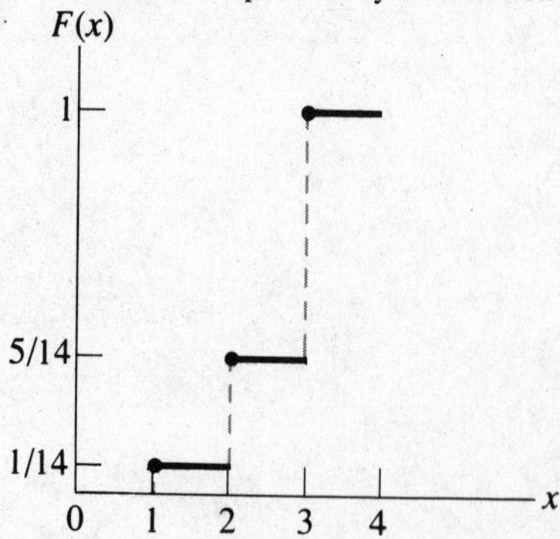

b.

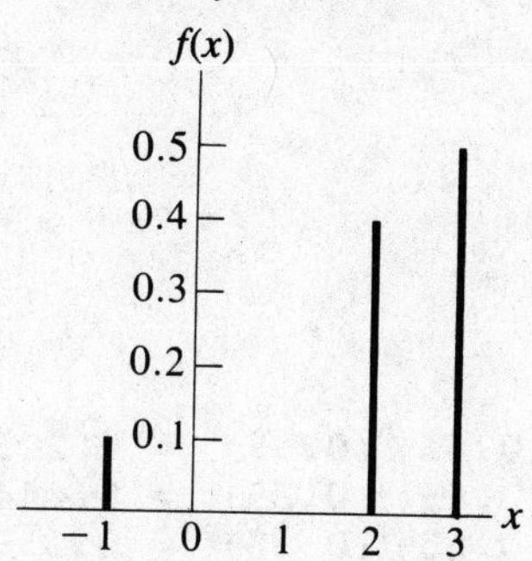

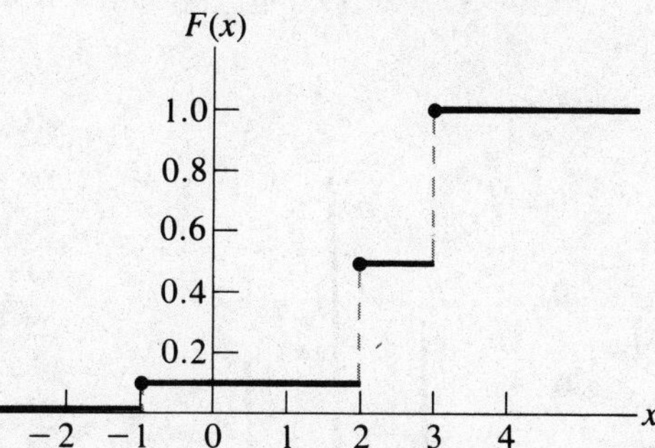

c. $\sum_x f(x) = 1$ and $f(x) \geq 0$ for all x in both functions.

3. a.

$$\sum_{x=1}^{3} \frac{k}{x+1} = 1$$

$$\frac{k}{1+1} + \frac{k}{2+1} + \frac{k}{3+1} = 1$$

$$\frac{k}{2} + \frac{k}{3} + \frac{k}{4} = 1$$

$$k = \frac{12}{13}$$

b.

$$\sum_{x=0}^{2} \frac{x^2 - x}{k} = 1$$

$$\frac{0}{k} + \frac{0}{k} + \frac{2}{k} = 1$$

$$k = 2$$

c.

$$\sum_{x=1}^{4} kx^2 = 1$$

$$k + 4k + 9k + 16k = 1$$

$$30k = 1$$

$$k = 1/30$$

4. a. Elements of the sample space: $\overline{K}\overline{K}\overline{K}$, $K\overline{K}\overline{K}$, $\overline{K}K\overline{K}$, $\overline{K}\overline{K}K$, $KK\overline{K}$, $K\overline{K}K$, $\overline{K}KK$, KKK

b. $\binom{3}{0} = \frac{3!}{0!3!} = 1$

$\binom{3}{1} = \frac{3!}{1!2!} = 3$

$\binom{3}{2} = \frac{3!}{2!1!} = 3$

$\binom{3}{3} = \frac{3!}{3!0!} = 1$

$$\begin{aligned}
P(X = 0) &= f(0) = 1(0.65)^3(0.35)^0 = 0.275 \\
P(X = 1) &= f(1) = 3(0.65)^2(0.35)^1 = 0.444 \\
P(X = 2) &= f(2) = 3(0.65)^1(0.35)^2 = 0.239 \\
P(X = 3) &= f(3) = 1(0.65)^0(0.35)^3 = \underline{0.042} \\
& \qquad\qquad\qquad\qquad\qquad\qquad\quad 1.000
\end{aligned}$$

c.

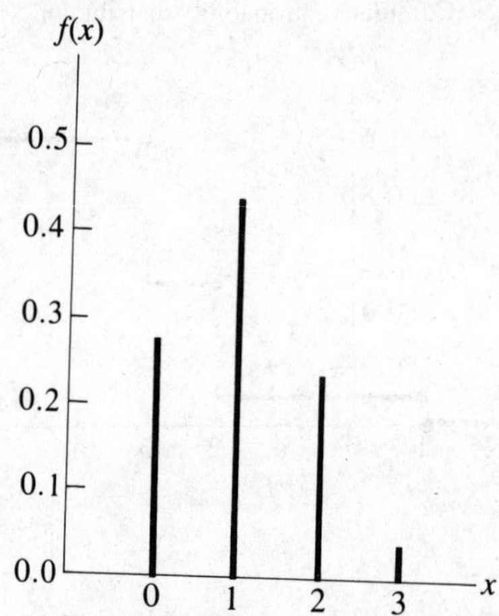

5. a. $\sum_x f(x) = 1$ and $0 \le f(x) \le 1$ for all x

b. $\frac{3}{15} = \frac{1}{5}$

c. $\frac{2}{15} + \frac{3}{15} + \frac{4}{15} = \frac{9}{15}$

d.

x	$f(x)$
1	$\frac{1}{15}$
2	$\frac{3}{15}$
3	$\frac{6}{15}$
4	$\frac{10}{15}$
5	1

6. $f(1) = \frac{1}{25}$; $f(2) = \frac{3}{25}$; $f(3) = \frac{5}{25} = \frac{1}{5}$; $f(4) = \frac{7}{25}$; $f(5) = \frac{9}{25}$

Exercises 3.3

1. $f(x) = 1/38$, $x = 00, 0, 1, \ldots, 36$

2. a. $f(x) = 1/96$, $x = 1, \ldots, 96$
   b. 70/96
   c. 40/96
   d. 41/96
   e. 25/96

3. $f(x) = \frac{1}{51}$; $x = 150, 151, \ldots, 200$.

   a. $\frac{30}{51} = \frac{10}{17}$

   b. $\frac{5}{51}$

   c. $\frac{10}{51}$

   d. $\frac{1}{51}$

Exercises 3.4

Although tables can be used, analytical solutions are given here. For example in exercise 1(a), from Table A-2, $P(3) = 0.2787$ for $n = 8$ and $p = 0.40$.

1. a. $\binom{8}{5}(0.40)^3(0.60)^5 = 0.2787$

   b. $\sum_{x=5}^{8}\binom{8}{x}(0.40)^{8-x}(0.60)^x = 0.5941$

   c. No, stock price movements cannot ordinarily be considered independent. Therefore, the binomial distribution is not the appropriate probability distribution.

2. $\binom{4}{3}(0.85)^1(0.15)^3 = 0.0115$

   Assuming independent trials means that the probability of being awarded a contract is not affected by previous biddings.

3. $\binom{2}{0}(0.60)^2(0.40)^0 = 0.36$

   $\binom{2}{1}(0.60)^1(0.40)^1 = 0.48$

   $\binom{2}{2}(0.60)^0(0.40)^2 = 0.16$

4. $\binom{10}{10}\left(\frac{16}{34}\right)^{10} = 0.0005$ The feat is highly unlikely.

5. a. $\binom{5}{5}\left(\frac{2}{3}\right)^0\left(\frac{1}{3}\right)^5 = 0.0041$

   b. $\sum_{x=2}^{3}\binom{3}{x}\left(\frac{2}{3}\right)^{3-x}\left(\frac{1}{3}\right)^x = 0.2593$

c. $\binom{10}{10}\left(\frac{1}{3}\right)^{10}$ = 0.00002

d. The outcomes on successive days of trading are independent.

6. $\sum_{x=2}^{10}\binom{10}{x}(0.95)^{10-x}(0.05)^{x} = 0.0861$

The probability is less than 10%; therefore, she should contract with Forte Iron.

7. $\binom{10}{7}(0.2)^{3}(0.8)^{7} = 0.2013$

8. $\binom{4}{2}\left(\frac{1}{3}\right)^{2}\left(\frac{2}{3}\right)^{2} + \binom{4}{3}\left(\frac{1}{3}\right)^{1}\left(\frac{2}{3}\right)^{3} = 0.6913$

9. a. $f(x) = \binom{3}{x}(0.75)^{3-x}(0.25)^{x}$

x	$F(x)$
0	0.4219
1	0.8438
2	0.9844
3	1.0000

b. $\binom{3}{2}(0.75)^{1}(0.25)^{2} = 0.1406$

10. $\binom{5}{0}\left(\frac{5}{6}\right)^{5}\left(\frac{1}{6}\right)^{0}$ = 3,125/7,776

$\binom{5}{5}\left(\frac{5}{6}\right)^{0}\left(\frac{1}{6}\right)^{5}$ = 1/7,776

11. a. $\binom{10}{1}(0.90)^{9}(0.10)^{1} = 0.3874$

b. $\binom{10}{1}(0.50)^{9}(0.50)^{1} = 0.0097$

c. $\binom{10}{1}(0.60)^{9}(0.40)^{1} = 0.0404$

12.

	p = 0.30	p = 0.50	p = 0.70
x	$f(x)$	$f(x)$	$f(x)$
0	0.1681	0.0312	0.0024
1	0.3601	0.1563	0.0284
2	0.3087	0.3125	0.1323
3	0.1323	0.3125	0.3087
4	0.0284	0.1563	0.3601
5	0.0024	0.0312	0.1681

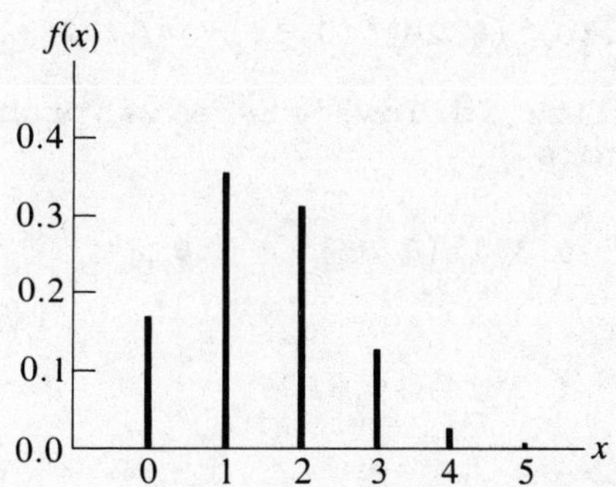

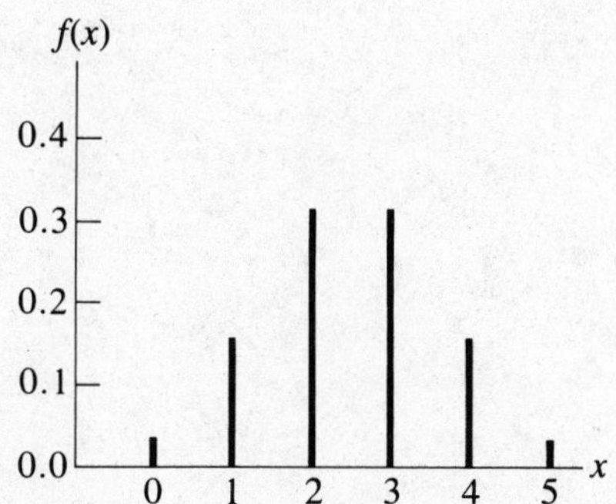

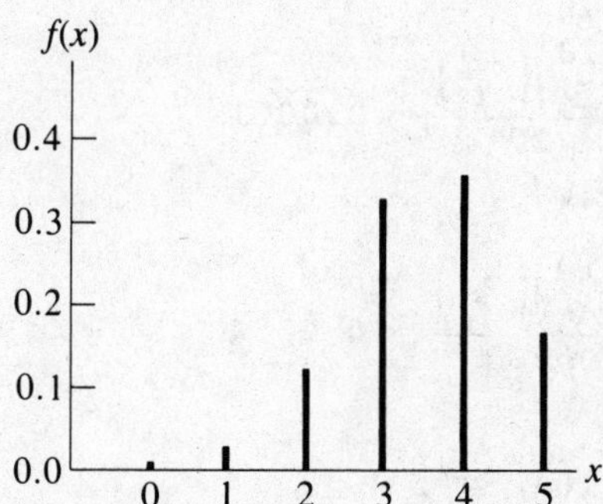

The binomial distribution becomes increasingly skewed to the left for all values of $p < 0.50$ and skewed to the right for all values of $p > 0.50$ (see figure).

13. $\sum_{x=0}^{10} \binom{50}{x} (0.75)^{50-x} (0.25)^{x}$

14. a. $\binom{16}{1} (0.90)^{15} (0.10)^{1} = 0.3294$

b. $\binom{16}{1} (0.80)^{15} (0.20)^{1} = 0.1126$

c. $\binom{16}{1} (0.75)^{15} (0.25)^{1} = 0.0535$

15. a. $\binom{3}{0} (0.75)^{3} (0.25)^{0} = 0.4219$

b. $\sum_{x=0}^{2} \binom{3}{x} (0.75)^{3-x} (0.25)^{x} = 0.9844$

Exercises 3.5

1. $\frac{12!}{2!4!6!} (0.01)^{2} (0.05)^{4} (0.94)^{6} = 0.000006$

Yes, this outcome is highly unlikely.

2. $\frac{15!}{3!4!6!2!}(0.40)^3(0.30)^4(0.20)^6(0.10)^2 = 0.002$

Since this probability is low, there is probably something wrong in the distribution of errors.

3. a. $\frac{20!}{10!8!2!}(0.65)^{10}(0.30)^8(0.05)^2 = 0.018$

b. $\sum_{x=0}^{10}\binom{20}{x}(0.70)^{20-x}(0.30)^x = 0.9829$

Exercises 3.6

1. a. $\frac{\binom{10}{5}\binom{10}{1}}{\binom{20}{6}} = 0.0001$

b. $\frac{\binom{10}{0}\binom{10}{6}}{\binom{20}{6}} = 0.0054$

c. $\frac{\binom{10}{2}\binom{5}{1}\binom{5}{3}}{\binom{20}{6}} = 0.058$

2. $\frac{\binom{13}{3}\binom{13}{4}\binom{13}{5}\binom{13}{1}}{\binom{52}{13}}$

3. a. $\frac{\binom{4}{1}\binom{8}{2}}{\binom{12}{3}} + \frac{\binom{4}{2}\binom{8}{1}}{\binom{12}{3}} + \frac{\binom{4}{3}\binom{8}{0}}{\binom{12}{3}} = \frac{164}{220} = 0.745$

b. $\sum_{x=1}^{3}\binom{3}{x}\left(\frac{8}{12}\right)^{3-x}\left(\frac{4}{12}\right)^x = 0.704$

4. Probability of appointing Mr. Hedge:

$$\frac{\binom{7}{0}\binom{5}{3}}{\binom{12}{3}} = \frac{10}{220} = 0.045$$

Probability if only a majority vote were needed:

$$\frac{\binom{7}{1}\binom{5}{2}}{\binom{12}{3}} + \frac{\binom{7}{0}\binom{5}{3}}{\binom{12}{3}} = \frac{70 + 10}{220} = 0.364$$

5. a. $\frac{\binom{3}{0}\binom{7}{6}}{\binom{10}{6}} = \frac{7}{210} = 0.033$

b. $\dfrac{\binom{5}{3}\binom{3}{2}\binom{2}{1}}{\binom{10}{6}} = \dfrac{60}{210} = 0.286$

c. $\dfrac{\binom{5}{1}\binom{5}{5}}{\binom{10}{6}} = \dfrac{5}{210} = 0.024$

6. a. $\dfrac{\binom{2}{1}\binom{3}{1}\binom{1}{1}}{\binom{6}{3}} = \dfrac{6}{20} = 0.30$

b. $\dfrac{\binom{1}{1}\binom{5}{2}}{\binom{6}{3}} = \dfrac{10}{20} = 0.50$

c. $\dfrac{\binom{2}{2}\binom{4}{1}}{\binom{6}{3}} = \dfrac{4}{20} = 0.20$

7. $\dfrac{\binom{5}{2}\binom{6}{3}\binom{9}{1}}{\binom{20}{6}} = 0.0464$

Exercises 3.7

1. a. $f(5) = \dfrac{4^5 e^{-4}}{5!} = 0.156$

b. $f(10) = \dfrac{8^{10} e^{-8}}{10!} = 0.099$

c. The longer the time period, the larger the number of events that can occur.

2. $f(0) = \dfrac{6^0 e^{-6}}{0!} = 0.002$

3. a. $f(2) = \dfrac{2.8^2 e^{-2.8}}{2!} = 0.238$

b. $1 - \sum_{x=0}^{1} \dfrac{2.8^x e^{-2.8}}{x!} = 1 - 0.231 = 0.769$

c. $\sum_{x=0}^{2} \dfrac{2.8^x e^{-2.8}}{x!} = 0.469$

4. a. $f(12) = \dfrac{12^{12} e^{-12}}{12!} = 0.114$

b. $1 - \sum_{x=0}^{10} \dfrac{12^x e^{-12}}{x!} = 1 - 0.347 = 0.653$

c. $\sum_{x=0}^{5} \frac{12^x e^{-12}}{x!} = 0.020$

5. $\mu = np = (10{,}000)(0.0001) = 1$

$1 - \sum_{x=0}^{3} \frac{1^x e^{-1}}{x!} = 1 - 0.981 = 0.019$

6. a. (1) The probability that all computers will be working is

$$\binom{5}{5}(0.05)^0(0.95)^5 = 0.774$$

(2) The probability that at least three computers will not be working is

$$1 - \sum_{x=0}^{2}\binom{5}{x}(0.95)^{5-x}(0.05)^x = 1 - 0.9988 = 0.0012$$

Exercises 3.13

1. $E(X) = 2\left(\frac{1}{2}\right) + 4\left(\frac{1}{2}\right)^2 + 8\left(\frac{1}{2}\right)^3 = \$3.00$

2. $E(\text{gain}) = (\$315)(0.97) + (-\$9{,}685)(0.03) = \$15$

No. On any single policy, the company will either earn the premium of $315 or pay out $9,685 ($10,000 - $315). The $15 represents the average return per policy if an infinite number of policies are issued.

3. Net profits are in thousands of dollars.

a.
$$\begin{aligned} E(\text{net profit A}) &= (0.3)(\$9{,}000) + (0.4)(\$10{,}000) \\ &\quad + (0.3)(\$11{,}000) \\ &= \$10{,}000 \end{aligned}$$

$$\begin{aligned} E(\text{net profit B}) &= (0.1)(\$8{,}000) + (0.2)(\$9{,}000) \\ &\quad + (0.4)(\$10{,}000) + (0.2)(\$11{,}000) \\ &\quad + (0.1)(\$12{,}000) \\ &= \$10{,}000 \end{aligned}$$

b.
$$\begin{aligned} \text{VAR(net profit A)} &= (\$9{,}000 - \$10{,}000)^2(0.3) \\ &\quad + (\$10{,}000 - \$10{,}000)^2(0.4) \\ &\quad + (\$11{,}000 - \$10{,}000)^2(0.3) \\ &= 600{,}000 \end{aligned}$$

$$\begin{aligned} \text{VAR(net profit B)} &= (\$8{,}000 - \$10{,}000)^2(0.1) \\ &\quad + (\$9{,}000 - \$10{,}000)^2(0.2) \\ &\quad + (\$10{,}000 - \$10{,}000)^2(0.4) \\ &\quad + (\$11{,}000 - \$10{,}000)^2(0.2) \\ &\quad + (\$12{,}000 - \$10{,}000)^2(0.1) \\ &= 1{,}200{,}000 \end{aligned}$$

Since the expected net profits of the two investments are the same and the variance of investment A is only one-half that of B, risk avoiders or risk neutral investors would prefer investment A.

4. a.
$$\begin{aligned} R(0) &= -\$3{,}000 \\ R(1) &= \$5{,}000(1) - \$1{,}000(2) = \$3{,}000 \\ R(2) &= \$5{,}000(2) - \$1{,}000(1) = \$9{,}000 \\ R(3) &= \$5{,}000(3) = \$15{,}000 \\ R(4) &= \$5{,}000(3) = \$15{,}000 \end{aligned}$$

b. $E(3) = \frac{10}{20}(-\$3,000) + \frac{2}{20}(\$3,000) + \frac{4}{20}(\$9,000) + \frac{3}{20}(\$15,000) + \frac{1}{20}(\$15,000)$

$= \$3,600$

$\text{VAR}(3) = \frac{10}{20}(-\$3,000 - \$3,600)^2 + \frac{2}{20}(\$3,000 - \$3,600)^2 + \frac{4}{20}(\$9,000 - \$3,600)^2 + \frac{3}{20}(\$15,000 - \$3,600)^2 + \frac{1}{20}(\$15,000 - \$3,600)^2$

$= 53,640,000$

$\sigma(3) = \$7,324$

c. Assuming that Heavy Machineries, Inc., desires to maximize expected monetary returns, the optimal number of pieces of equipment to be sent can be obtained by comparing the expected returns for all decisions (that is, to send 1, 2, 3, or 4 pieces). The optimal decision is associated with the highest return.

5. a. Since $\mu_A = \mu_B = 1.0$, the salesperson can expect to sell the same number of cars at both dealers. However, $\sigma_A^2 > \sigma_B^2$. Therefore, dealer B offers more consistent sales.

$\text{VAR}(A) = (0 - 1)^2(0.4) + (1 - 1)^2(0.3) + (2 - 1)^2(0.2) + (3 - 1)^2(0.1) = 1.0$

$\text{VAR}(B) = (0 - 1)^2(0.2) + (1 - 1)^2(1.6) + (2 -1)^2(0.2) + (0 - 1)^2(0.0) = 0.4$

b. Let $W = 100 + 100B$

$E(W) = E(\$100 + 100B) = E(100) + 100E(B) = \$100 + \$100(1) = \$200$

$\text{VAR}(W) = \sigma^2(\$100 + 100B) = \sigma^2(\$100) + \sigma^2(100B) = 0 + (100)^2\sigma^2(B)$

$= 10,000(0.4) = 4,000$

$\sigma(W) = \sqrt{4,000} = \$63.25$

6. μ = mean without fifth outlet = $\mu_1 + \mu_2 + \mu_3 + \mu_4$
= \$6,500 + \$6,200 + \$6,000 + \$5,800 = \$24,500

μ = mean with fifth outlet = $\mu + \mu_5$ = \$24,500 + 8,000 = \$32,500

The variance of total sales will increase by 15,000 with the acquisition of the fifth outlet; that variance will amount to 47,300 per month.

7. a. $E(Y) = 8(0.3) + 10(0.5) + 11.5(0.1) + 12(0.1)$
= 9.75 million pounds

$\text{VAR}(Y) = (8 - 9.75)^2(0.3) + (10 - 9.75)^2(0.5) + (11.5 - 9.75)^2(0.1) + (12 - 9.75)^2(0.1)$
$= 1.7625$

b. $E(Y') = E(Y + 5) = E(Y) + 5 = 9.75 + 5 = 14.75$ million pounds. Thus, the expected value of national income will reach 14.75 million pounds.

8. a. $E(T) = (0)(0.02) + 1(0.04) + 2(0.12) + 3(0.20) + 4(0.30) + 5(0.20) + 6(0.12)$
= 3.8 copies per week

$\text{VAR}(T) = (0 - 3.8)^2(0.02) + (1 - 3.8)^2(0.04) + (2 - 3.8)^2(0.12) + (3 - 3.8)^2(0.20) + (4 - 3.8)^2(0.30) + (5 - 3.8)^2(0.20) + (6 - 3.8)^2(0.12)$
$= 2.0$

$$E(S) = 0(0.10) + 1(0.10) + 2(0.10) + 3(0.15) + 4(0.20) + 5(0.15) + 6(0.20)$$
$$= 3.5 \text{ copies per week}$$

$$\text{VAR}(S) = (0 - 3.5)^2(0.10) + (1 - 3.5)^2(0.10) + (2 - 3.5)^2(0.10) + (3 - 3.5)^2(0.15) + (4 - 3.5)^2(0.20) + (5 - 3.5)^2(0.15) + (6 - 3.5)^2(0.20)$$
$$= 3.75$$

$E(T) > E(S)$ and $\text{VAR}(T) < \text{VAR}(S)$

b. $\text{Profit}(T) = (0.40)(3.8) - (0.15)(6) = \$0.62$
$\text{Profit}(S) = (0.60)(3.5) - (0.30)(6) + (0.05)(2.5) = \$0.425$

c. *TV Times.*

9. $E(X) = (7)(0.08) + (8)(0.13) + (9)(0.21) + (10)(0.24) + (11)(0.13) + (12)(0.10) + (13)(0.06) + (14)(0.05) = 10$

10. Let $X_1, X_2, \ldots, X_{12}$ represent the net profit per month for the 12 stores. Then $X_1 + X_2 + \cdots + X_{12}$ = total net profit per month for the 12 stores combined.

$$E(X_1 + X_2 + \cdots + X_{12}) = E(X_1) + E(X_2) + \cdots + E(X_{12})$$
$$= 12(\$6500) = \$78{,}000$$
$$\text{VAR}(X_1 + X_2 + \cdots + X_{12}) = \text{VAR}(X_1) + \text{VAR}(X_2) + \cdots + \text{VAR}(X_{12})$$
$$= 12(30{,}000) = 360{,}000$$
$$\sigma(X_1 + X_2 + \cdots + X_{12}) = \$600$$

11. $X_i = \begin{cases} + \$125 \text{ if numbers 1 through 12 occur on } i\text{th roll} \\ - \$60 \text{ if numbers other than 1 through 12 occur on } i\text{th roll} \end{cases}$

$$E(X_1) = (\$125)\left(\frac{12}{38}\right) + (-\$60)\left(\frac{26}{38}\right) = -\frac{30}{19} = -\$1.58$$

$X_1 + X_2 + \cdots + X_{500}$ = Total profit (loss)

$$E(X_1 + X_2 + \cdots + X_{500}) = E(X_1) + E(X_2) + \cdots + E(X_{500}) = (500)E(X_i) = 500(-\frac{30}{19})$$
$$= -\$789.47$$

12. $\mu = E(X) = \Sigma\, xf(x) = 0.0500$; $\text{VAR}(X) = \Sigma\,(x - \mu)^2 f(x) = 0.000592$; $\sigma(X) = 0.0243$; expected percentage of users affected: 5%; standard deviation: 2.43%

13. $(\$9)E(X) - 8(\$5) = \$9[(5)(0.2) + (6)(0.4) + (7)(0.3) + (8)(0.1)] - \$40 = \$9(6.3) - \$40.00 = \$16.70$

14. $$E(\text{total time}) = E(\text{I} + \text{II} + \text{III} + \text{IV}) = E(\text{I}) + E(\text{II}) + E(\text{III}) + E(\text{IV})$$
$$= 5 + 14 + 8 + 3 = 30 \text{ weeks}$$
$$\text{VAR}(\text{total time}) = \sigma^2(\text{I} + \text{II} + \text{III} + \text{IV}) = \sigma^2(\text{I}) + \sigma^2(\text{II}) + \sigma^2(\text{III}) + \sigma^2(\text{IV})$$
$$= 4 + 25 + 9 + 1 = 39$$
$$\sigma(\text{total time}) = \sqrt{39} = 6.24 \text{ weeks}$$

Exercises 3.15

1. A_1 = under 2,000 cases, A_2 = at least 2,000 cases, B_1 = ordinary bottles, B_2 = ordinary cans, B_3 = flip-top cans, B_4 = screw-top bottles.

a. $P(A_2 \text{ and } B_3) = \frac{10}{200} = \frac{1}{20}$

$P(B_3) = \frac{40}{200} = \frac{1}{5}$

$P(A_2|B_3) = \frac{10}{40} = \frac{1}{4}$

b. $P(A_1) = \frac{140}{200} = 0.7$

$P(A_2) = \frac{60}{200} = 0.3$

$P(B_1) = P(B_2) = \frac{60}{200} = 0.3$

$P(B_3) = P(B_4) = \frac{40}{200} = 0.2$

c. $P(A_1|B_1) = \frac{45}{60} = 0.75$ $P(A_2|B_1) = \frac{15}{60} = 0.25$

d. Yes; $f(\text{sales})g(\text{packaging}) \neq f(\text{sales, packaging})$

e.

Sales	Ordinary Bottles	Ordinary Cans	Flip-top Cans	Screw-top Bottles	Total
Under 2,000 cases	42	42	28	28	140
At least 2,000 cases	18	18	12	12	60
Total	60	60	60	40	200

2. Yes; $P(\text{for}|\text{skilled}) = 275/600 \neq P(\text{for}) = 500/1{,}400$. A higher proportion of skilled employees than unskilled employees is in favor of the labor proposal.

3. Let A_1 = Jellied cranberry A_2 = Whole cranberry
C_1 = Convenience-oriented C_2 = Enthusiastic
C_3 = Decorator C_4 = Disinterested

a. (1) $P(C_3 \text{ and } A_1) = \frac{19}{200} = 0.095$

(2) $P(C_2) = \frac{69}{200} = 0.345$

(3) $P(C_1|A_1) = \frac{35}{100} = 0.35$

b. $P(A_1) = \frac{100}{200} = 0.50$ $P(C_1) = \frac{65}{200} = 0.325$

$P(A_2) = \frac{100}{200} = 0.50$ $P(C_2) = \frac{69}{200} = 0.345$

$P(C_3) = \frac{35}{200} = 0.175$

$P(C_4) = \frac{31}{200} = 0.155$

c. Yes; $P(\text{sauce type})P(\text{user type}) \neq P(\text{sauce type and user type})$

4. a.

$y \backslash x$	0	1	2	3
0	0	2/56	4/56	6/56
1	1/56	3/56	5/56	7/56
2	4/56	6/56	8/56	10/56

b.

x	$f(x)$	y	$g(y)$
0	5/56	0	12/56
1	11/56	1	16/56
2	17/56	2	28/56
3	23/56		1
	1		

c.

y	$g(y\|0)$	$g(y\|1)$	$g(y\|2)$	$g(y\|3)$
0	0	2/11	4/17	6/23
1	1/5	3/11	5/17	7/23
2	4/5	6/11	8/17	10/23

d. No. $f(x)g(y) \neq f(x, y)$

5. a. $E(X) = (0)(0.2) + (1)(0.6) + (2)(0.2) = 1.0$
$E(Y) = (0)(0.2) + (1)(0.6) + (2)(0.2) = 1.0$
$E(X + Y) = E(X) + E(Y) = 1.0 + 1.0 = 2.0$

The expected number of sales for Exotic Motors and Phlegmatic Motors combined is 2.0 per day.

b. $E(Y|X = 1) = (0)1/6 + (1)5/6 + (2)(0) = 5/6$ sales per day

$\text{VAR}(\overline{X} = 1) = (0)^2 1/6 + (1)^2 5/6 + (2)^2(0) - (5/6)^2 = 5/36$

$\sigma(Y|X = 1) = \sqrt{5/36} \approx 0.37$ sales per day

c. Profit = \$1,500X + \$1,200Y. The only cases in which profit would exceed \$4,000 are when $X = 2$ and $Y = 1$ and $X = 2$ and $Y = 2$. The probability = 0 + 0.2 = 0.2.

CHAPTER 4

Exercises 4.2

See the discussion in section 4.2 for the answer to question 2.

Exercises 4.4

1. See the discussion in section 4.4.

2. See the discussion in section 4.4

3. a. Assume that a control group of headache sufferers who took no pain-relieving drugs was established. It is possible that more than 90% of this group could have reported reduced pain after 2 hours. Such a finding would provide evidence that taking no pain reliever is as effective as aspirin in relieving headache pain.
   b. One possible control would be other brokers who may have had more than 85% of their recommendations outperform market expectations. Another possible control group would be a random selection of stocks, which might show that 85% performed better than market expectations. Either control group would dispute the broker's claim of superior investment insight.
   c. A control group of farmers who did not use Moregro might have had a greater than 10% increase in crop yield last year, which would not only dispute the advertising claim but would also produce evidence that Moregro decreases crop yield.

4. a. The control group would consist of athletes who perform the same exercises, but who are not given the new heat treatment.
   b. The control group would be a sample of children who are given the information, but without visual aids.
   c. No control group is needed to test this assertion. A large and ongoing sample to find any marathon runners who have suffered a heart attack (which would disprove the hypothesis) is needed.

5. If the object of the study was to determine whether the advertising campaign would increase consumption by current users, then both the experimental and the control groups should have been composed of individuals currently using the product. The experimental group would be exposed to the campaign; the control group would not be exposed to the campaign.

6. The director used those employees who had attended the previous year's party as the universe. The director's sample was biased because employees who thought spouses should be included probably had a lower attendance rate than other employees—such as singles or married persons who did not prefer the inclusion of spouses. The subgroup of employees who attended the Christmas party last year undoubtedly differed from the "all other employees" group with respect to preferences for an "employees only" party.

7. a. If less than 6% of all persons in the United States in the given year belonged to families with annual incomes of at least $10,000, the

statistic indicates a higher incidence of polio for this group than for lower income groups. A direct comparison could be made between the incidence of polio in families with annual incomes of at least $10,000 (treatment group) and the corresponding incidence of polio in families with incomes of $10,000 and under (control group).

b. The study could conclude that women were worse students than men if women constituted less than 20% of the student body in this university. A direct comparison could be made between the failure rate for women (treatment group) and the corresponding failure rate for men (control group).

c. Assume that we define a control group consisting of cold sufferers who use no cold remedy at all and that more than 95% of this control group were free of their colds within a one-week period. This would constitute evidence that the cold preparation is ineffective in shortening the duration of the cold.

8. Yes, probably both sampling and systematic errors are present. Sampling error would exist in a random sample of 10,000 compared with the population of 200,000 subscribers. Systematic error is probably introduced because of the difference between the attitudes of the 1,500 respondents and the corresponding attitudes of the total sample of 10,000.

9. a. Both systematic and random errors. The systematic error arises from the fact that the student lounge is the only area in the building where smoking is permitted. Therefore, the study includes an overrepresentation of smokers compared with the percentage in the general student population. The random error arises from the difference in the percentage of smokers in the sample of 100 students and the percentage of smokers among all students who use the lounge.

b. Random error. As sample size increases, the average life of the tubes in the sample would tend to be closer to the "true" average life. On the other hand, if the tubes in the particular stores included in the sample had a lower average life than was true for this type of vacuum tube, then clearly, systematic error might be present as well.

c. Both systematic and random errors. The systematic error component is due to inaccurate scales. If only this component were present, we would expect the average weight to be 1.1 pounds. We attribute the residual error to chance fluctuations in the sampling and measurement of the contents of 50 cans.

d. Systematic and random errors. A systematic error component is introduced because people who feel strongly one way or the other on an issue (in this case, those who rate the services bad or good) tend to have higher response rates than others. Random error is also introduced because of sample size.

Exercises 4.5

1. a. A census of the students in the class appears to be appropriate. Any type of sample would deprive some students of the opportunity to express an opinion, which from the standpoint of fairness, would be inadvisable.

b. A sample of the subscribers would be advisable. The greater accuracy of a census would probably not warrant the additional cost.

c. The total number of customers would be an important factor. If this number were relatively small, a census would be preferable. If the number were large, a sample would doubtless be a better solution.

d. A census would be preferable. Since there are only 25 firms, the trade association could obtain the employment data from each company.

2. a. The universe sampled was all of those parents with children in Lower Fenwick public schools. However, a simple random sample of pupils did not constitute a simple random sample of the parent population. Parents with more than one child in the public schools had a higher probability of inclusion in the sample than did parents with only one child in these schools.

b. See part (a).
c. We would not approve the universe studied. If the school board wished to ascertain voter opinion, it should have sampled the population of voters in Lower Fenwick, many of whom may not have children in the public schools. A relevant sampling frame would have been a current list of registered voters in Lower Fenwick.

3. a. False. No objective measure of random error is possible with judgment sampling, because of the nonrandom method of sampling.
b. False. Sampling can reduce the time spent and the likelihood of error.
c. True.

CHAPTER 5

Exercises 5.1

1. a.

Possible Samples	Sample Mean ($\overline{X}$)	Probability $P(\overline{X})$
(4,5)	4.5	0.1
(4,6)	5.0	0.1
(4,7)(5,6)	5.5	0.2
(4,8)(5,7)	6.0	0.2
(5,8)(6,7)	6.5	0.2
(6,8)	7.0	0.1
(7,8)	7.5	0.1
		1.0

b. $E(\overline{X})$ = (4.5)(0.1) + (5.0)(0.1) + (5.5)(0.2) + (6.0)(0.2) + (6.5)(0.2) + (7.0)(0.1) + (7.5)(0.1) = 6 sales

$$\mu = \frac{4 + 5 + 6 + 7 + 8}{5} = 6 \text{ sales}$$

The mean of the sampling distribution of means is equal to the mean of the population values.

c. <u>Between 5 and 7 sales</u>
Proportion of population elements = 3/5 = 60%
Proportion of sample means = 8/10 = 80%

2. a.

Possible Samples	Sample Mean ($\overline{X}$)	Probability $P(\overline{X})$
(4,4)	4.0	1/15
(4,5)	4.5	1/15
(4,6)(5,5)	5.0	2/15
(4,7)(5,6)	5.5	2/15
(4,8)(5,7)(6,6)	6.0	3/15
(5,8)(6,7)	6.5	2/15
(6,8)(7,7)	7.0	2/15
(7,8)	7.5	1/15
(8,8)	8.0	1/15
		1

b. $E(\overline{X}) = (4.0)(1/15) + (4.5)(1/15) + \ldots + (8.0)(1/15) = 6$

$$\mu = \frac{4 + 5 + 6 + 7 + 8}{5} = 6$$

The sample mean is an unbiased estimator of the population mean in simple random sampling, with or without replacement.

Exercises 5.3

1. a.

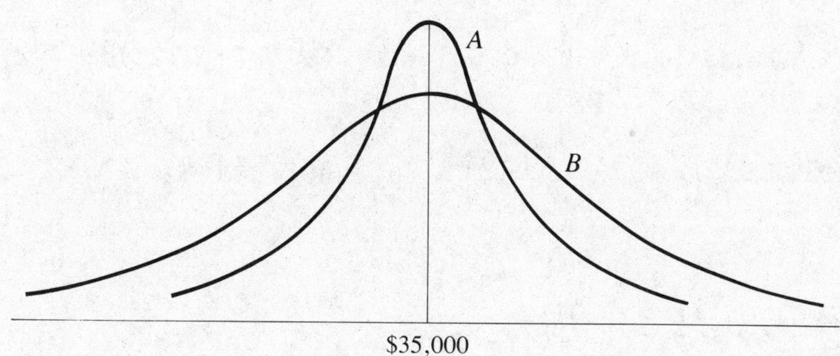

b.

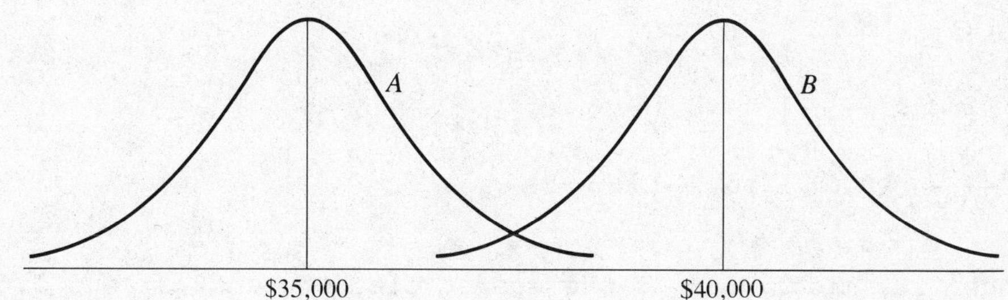

2. a. 0.5000
   b. 0.0062
   c. 0.8664
   d. 0.6170
   e. 0.0228
   f. 0.8413

3. a. $P(z \geq 1)$
   b. $P(z < -1.5)$
   c. $P(-2 \leq z \leq 2)$
   d. $P(-1.25 \leq z \leq 1.25)$
   e. $P(z > 1.50) + P(z < -1.5)$
   f. $P(z < 2)$

4. a. 0.50

   b. $P = 2(0.4772) = 0.9544$

   c. z of 0.350 is 1.04

   $$-1.04 = \frac{x - 450}{75}$$

   $$x = 372$$

5. a. $P\left(z > \frac{0 - 0}{1}\right) = 0.5$

   b. $P(\epsilon_t < -2.00) + P(\epsilon_t \geq 2.00)$

   $$= P\left(z \leq \frac{-2.00 - 0}{1}\right) + P\left(z \geq \frac{2.00 - 0}{1}\right)$$

   $$= 0.0456$$

c. $P(P_t - P_{t-1} \le 1.50) = P(\epsilon_t \le 1.50)$

$= P\left(z \le \frac{1.50 - 0}{1}\right) = 0.9332$

6. a. $P\left(\frac{2.0 - 3}{1} < z < \frac{4.0 - 3}{1}\right) = 0.6826$

b. $P\left(z < \frac{2.8 - 3}{1}\right) = 0.4207$

$P\left(\frac{4.5 - 6}{2} < z < \frac{6.5 - 6}{2}\right) = 0.3721$

$P\{(X < 2.8) \text{ and } (4.5 < Y < 6.5)\} = (0.4207)(0.3721)$
$= 0.1565$

c. $P\left(z < \frac{2.8 - 3}{1}\right)P\left(z > \frac{3.0 - 6.0}{2}\right) = (0.4207)(0.9332)$

$= 0.3926$

d. $P\{X < 2.8) \text{ or } (Y > 3.0)\}$
$= P(X < 2.8) + P(Y > 3.0) - P[(X < 2.8) \text{ and } (Y > 3.0)]$
$= (0.4207) + (0.9332) - (0.3926)$
$= 0.9613$

e. $2P\left(0 \le z \le \frac{X - 3}{1}\right) = 0.51$

$P\left(0 \le z \le \frac{X - 3}{1}\right) = 0.255$

$\frac{(X - 3)}{1} = 0.69$ (from Table A-5)

$X = 3.69$

Hence, the middle 51% of the scores lie between 2.31 and 3.69.

7. a. 0.5

b. $P\left(z > \frac{40 - 36.8}{5.4}\right) = 0.2776$

c. $P\left(\frac{30 - 36.8}{5.4} \le z \le \frac{40 - 36.8}{5.4}\right) = 0.6186$

8. a. $P\left(z < \frac{21.5 - 18}{3}\right) = P(z < 1.17) = 0.8790$

b. $P\left(z \le \frac{16.5 - 18}{3}\right) = P(z \le -0.5) = 0.3085$

c. $P\left(z \le \frac{x - 18}{3}\right) = 0.0668 \qquad z = -1.5$

Therefore, $x = 18 - 1.5(3) = 13.5$ minutes.

Exercises 5.5

1. a. $P\left(z < \dfrac{445 - 450}{50/\sqrt{900}}\right) = 0.00135$

   b. Yes, it is a reasonable assertion.

2. a. $P\left(z > \dfrac{30,000 - 32,000}{1,500}\right) = 0.9082$

   b. $P\left(z > \dfrac{35,000 - 32,000}{1,500}\right) = 0.0228$

   c. $P\left(z > \dfrac{30,000 - 32,000}{1,500/\sqrt{4}}\right) = 0.9962$

3. Each week: $164 \pm 2(19)$, or 126 - 202

   Each month: $164 \pm 2(19/\sqrt{4}$, or 145 - 183

4. a. Disagree. The Central Limit Theorem applies to the distribution of the sample means, not to the population distribution.
   b. Agree.
   c. Disagree. The Central Limit Theorem applies to the approach of the sampling distribution of the mean to normality as *n* becomes large.

5. $P\left(z > \dfrac{40 - 38}{\sqrt{64/100}}\right) = 0.0062$

   No, because of the Central Limit Theorem.

6. $P\left(z \geq \dfrac{30 - 28}{\sqrt{81/100}}\right) = 0.0132$

   No, because of the Central Limit Theorem.

7. a. $P\left(z \geq \dfrac{34,000 - 36,000}{2500}\right) = P(z > -0.8) = 0.7881$

   b. $P\left(z > \dfrac{40,000 - 36,000}{2500}\right) = P(z > 1.6) = 0.0548$

   c. $P\left(z > \dfrac{34,000 - 36,000}{2500/\sqrt{8}}\right) = P(z > -2.26) = 0.9881$

8. Each week: $4500 \pm 2(450)$, or 3600 - 5400

   Each month: $4500 \pm 2(450/\sqrt{4})$, or 4050 - 4950

9. a. $z_0 = (\$3,000 - \$5,160)/(\$800/\sqrt{50}) = -1.41$

   $P(\overline{X} > 5,000) = P(z > -1.41) = 0.9207$

   b. $P(\overline{X} < 5,000) = P(z < -1.41) = 0.0793$

   c. $z_1 = (\$5,200 - 5,160)/(\$800/\sqrt{50}) = 0.35$

   $z_2 = (\$5,300 - 5,160)/(\$800/\sqrt{50}) = 1.24$

   $P(5,200 < \overline{X} < \$5,300) = P(0.35 < z < 1.24)$

   $= 0.3925 - 0.1368 = 0.2557$

10. Use the Central Limit Theorem

$z_0 = \$200/(2{,}000/\sqrt{100}) = 1$

$$P(|\overline{X} - \mu| > \$200) = P(|z| > 1) = 0.3174$$

Exercises 5.6

1. The number of affirmative replies, X, can have the values 0, 1, 2, …, 100.

$\mu_x = 20 \qquad \mu_{\bar{p}} = 0.20$

$\sigma_x^2 = 16 \qquad \sigma_{\bar{p}} = 0.04$

$\sigma_x = 4$

2. a.

p
0.00
0.17
0.33
0.50
0.67
0.83
1.00

b.

$f(\bar{p} \mid p = 0.90)$
0
0.0001
0.0012
0.0146
0.0984
0.3543
0.5314

c.

$f(\bar{p} \mid p = 0.5)$
0.0156
0.0938
0.2344
0.3124
0.2344
0.0938
0.0156

3.

$\mu_{n\bar{p}}$	$\sigma_{n\bar{p}}$
2 persons	$\sqrt{10(0.2)(0.8)} = 1.26$ persons
4 persons	$\sqrt{20(0.2)(0.8)} = 1.79$ persons
8 persons	$\sqrt{40(0.2)(0.8)} = 2.53$ persons

4. $\mu_{\bar{p}} = p = 0.25$

$$\sigma_{\bar{p}} = \sqrt{\frac{pq}{n}} = \sqrt{\frac{(0.25)(0.75)}{20}} = 0.0968$$

5. a. $\mu_{\bar{p}} = p = 0.05$

$\sigma_{\bar{p}} = \sqrt{pq/n} = \sqrt{(0.05)(0.95)/20} = 0.0487$

b. $\mu_{\bar{p}} = p = 0.05$

$\sigma_{\bar{p}} = \sqrt{pq/n} = \sqrt{(0.05)(0.95)/40} = 0.0345$

Exercises 5.7

1. a.

$$P(X \geq 2) = 1 - \binom{20}{0}(0.90)^{20}(0.10)^{0} - \binom{20}{1}(0.90)^{19}(0.10)^{1} = 1 - 0.3917 = 0.6083$$

b.

$$P\left(z \geq \frac{1.5 - 2.0}{\sqrt{(0.10)(0.90)(20)}}\right) = 0.6443$$

2. a. $P\left(\frac{5.5 - 6}{\sqrt{(0.15)(0.85)(40)}} \le z \le \frac{6.5 - 6}{\sqrt{(0.15)(0.85)(40)}}\right)$

$= P(-0.22 \le z \le 0.22) = 0.1742$

b. $P(z > 0.22) = 0.4129$

c. $P(z < -0.22) = 0.4129$

3. a. $P\left(\frac{0.5 - 5}{\sqrt{(0.2)(0.8)(25)}} \le z \le \frac{1.5 - 5}{\sqrt{(0.2)(0.8)(25)}}\right)$

$= P(-2.25 \le z \le -1.75) = 0.0279$

b. $P\left(\frac{1.5 - 5}{\sqrt{(0.2)(0.8)(25)}} \le z \le \frac{2.5 - 5}{\sqrt{(0.2)(0.8)(25)}}\right)$

$= P(-1.75 \le z \le -1.25) = 0.0655$

c. $P(-1.25 \le z \le -0.75) = 0.1210$

$P(-0.25 \le z \le 0.25) = 0.1974$

4. From Alaska: $P\left(z > \frac{90 - 100}{\sqrt{(0.25)(0.75)(400)}}\right)$

$= P(z > -1.15) = 0.8749$

From Texas: $P\left(z > \frac{90 - 80}{\sqrt{(0.2)(0.8)(400)}}\right)$

$= P(z > 1.25) = 0.1056$

5. a. $\mu_{\bar{x}} = \$512$; $\sigma_{\bar{x}} = \frac{\$150}{\sqrt{1,000}} \sqrt{\frac{5,024 - 1,000}{5,024 - 1}} \approx \$4.25$

b. $\mu_{\bar{x}} = \$564$; $\sigma_{\bar{x}} = \frac{\$150}{\sqrt{1,000}} \sqrt{\frac{10,244 - 1,000}{10,244 - 1}} \approx \$4.51$

c. The standard deviation in part (a) is smaller because the population is smaller than in part (b).

6. a. Using the binomial distribution, $p = 0.15$, $n = 10$, $x = 1$; $P(X = 1) = 0.3474$

b. $P\left(\frac{56 - 68}{12} \le z \le \frac{92 - 68}{12}\right) = P(-1 \le z \le 2) = 0.8185$

c. $P\left(\frac{70 - 68}{12/\sqrt{49}} \le z \le \frac{74 - 68}{12/\sqrt{49}}\right) = P(1.17 \le z \le 3.5) = 0.8779$

d. $P\left(z > \frac{x - 68}{12}\right) = 0.1357$; $z = 1.10$

$x = 68 + 1.10(12) = 81.2$

7. a. No, they are only the results for a particular sample.
   b. The sampling distribution comprises the means of all possible samples of six executives that could be selected, along with the associated probabilities.

$\mu_{\bar{x}} = 12$; $\sigma_{\bar{x}} = \sqrt{\frac{20 - 6}{20 - 1}}(3/\sqrt{6}) = 1.05$ hours per week

8. $z_0 = \dfrac{0.75 - 0.80}{\sqrt{\dfrac{(0.8)(0.2)}{100}}} = -1.25$

$P(\overline{p} \geq 0.75) = P(z \geq -1.25) = 0.8944$

9. a. Agree
   b. Disagree. The probability of obtaining heads on *exactly* half the tosses approaches 0 as the number of tosses approaches infinity.
   c. Disagree. The Central Limit Theorem applies to the distribution of the means of samples, not to the population distribution.
   d. Agree
   e. Disagree. The Central Limit Theorem applies to the approach of the sampling distribution of the mean to normality as n becomes large.

10. a. $\mu_{\bar{x}} = \$98{,}900$, $\sigma_{\bar{x}} = \dfrac{\$4210}{\sqrt{25}}\sqrt{\dfrac{100 - 25}{100 - 1}} = \$732.87$

    b. $\mu_{\bar{x}} = \$98{,}900$, $\sigma_{\bar{x}} = \dfrac{\$4210}{\sqrt{50}}\sqrt{\dfrac{100 - 50}{100 - 1}} = \$423.12$

    c. $\mu_{\bar{x}} = \$98{,}900$, $\sigma_{\bar{x}} = 0$, since only one sample is possible.

REVIEW EXERCISES FOR CHAPTERS 1 THROUGH 5

1. a. $\sigma_{\bar{p}} = \sqrt{\dfrac{(.20)(.80)}{50}} = 0.0566$

   $z = \dfrac{0.25 - 0.20}{0.0566} = 0.88$

   $P(\bar{p} \geq 0.25) = P(z \geq 0.88) = 0.5000 - 0.3106 = 0.1894$

   b. $z_1 = \dfrac{\$18,500 - \$20,000}{1,500} = -1$

   $z_2 = \dfrac{\$23,000 - \$20,000}{\$1,500} = 2$

   $P(-1 \leq z \leq 2) = 0.3413 + 0.4772 = 0.8185$

   c. $P(0 \leq z \leq 0.81) = 0.500 - 0.209 = 0.291$

   Therefore, the z value that corresponds to an area of 0.291 is 0.81.

   $x_0 = \$20,000 + 0.81(\$1,500) = \$21,215$

2. a. $P(X \geq 1.2) = P(z \geq \dfrac{1.2 - 1.06}{0.3140}) = P(z \geq .45) = 0.5 - 0.1736 = 0.3264$

   Empirical probability = 12/21 = 0.57. Not a good approximation.

   b. Mode = 1.2
   Median = 1.2 (value of 10.5^{th} item)

3. a. $z = (147 - 120)/20 = 1.35$
   $P(x > 147) = P(z > 1.35) = 0.5000 - 0.4115 = 0.0885$

   b. $\sigma_{\bar{x}} = 20/\sqrt{36} = 3.33$

   $z = \dfrac{125 - 120}{3.33} = 1.50$

   $P(115 \leq \bar{x} \leq 125) = P(-1.5 \leq z \leq 1.5) = 2(0.4332) = 0.8664$

   c. $\sigma_{\bar{p}} = \sqrt{\dfrac{(0.10)(0.90)}{100}} = 0.03$

   $z = \dfrac{0.14 - 0.10}{0.03} = 1.33$

   $P(\bar{p} > 0.14) = P(z > 1.33) = 0.5000 - 0.4082 = 0.0918$

4. a. $\dfrac{\binom{3}{2}\binom{17}{0}}{\binom{20}{2}} = \dfrac{3}{\dfrac{20!}{18!2!}} = \left(\dfrac{3}{20}\right)\left(\dfrac{2}{19}\right) = 0.016$ or $\dfrac{\binom{2}{2}\binom{18}{1}}{\binom{20}{3}} = 0.016$

b. Poisson distribution

$\mu = np = (50)(0.016) = 0.80$
$P(X \geq 1) = 1 - F(0) = 1 - 0.449 = 0.551$ (Table A-3 for $\mu = 0.8$)

or by binomial distribution

$P(X \geq 1) = 1 - (0.984)^{50} = 0.554$

c. $E(X) = (-\$1)(0.984) + (\$50)(0.016) = -\$0.184$

5. a. $\binom{10}{5}\binom{5}{5} = 252$

b. $\dfrac{\binom{2}{2}\binom{8}{3}}{\binom{10}{5}} = 0.44$

c. $\dfrac{\binom{5}{3}\binom{3}{2}\binom{2}{0}}{\binom{10}{5}} = 0.119$

6. a. $z_0 = \dfrac{0 - 5}{9} = -0.56$

$P(X \leq 0) = P(z < -0.56) = 0.5000 - 0.2123 = 0.2877 \approx 0.29$

Using the Binomial Distribution

$p = 0.29$ (probability of early arrival)
$q = 0.71$
$n = 5$
$P(X = 3) = \binom{5}{3}(.71)^2(.29)^3 \approx 0.12$

b. $\sigma_{\bar{x}} = \dfrac{\sigma}{\sqrt{n}} = \dfrac{9}{\sqrt{9}} = 3$

$z_0 = \dfrac{4 - 5}{3} = -1.3 = -0.33$

$P(X \geq 4) = P(z > -0.33) = 0.1293 + 0.5000 = 0.6293$

7. a. $p = 0.30$, $n = 20$; $P(X \geq 4) = 1 - F(3) = 1 - 0.1071 = .8929$ (Binomial)

b. $\mu = np = (20)(.30) = 6$ $P(X \geq 4 = 1 - F(3) = 1 - 0.151 = 0.849$ (Poisson)

c. $\mu = (20)(.30) = 6$ $P(X \geq 4) = P(z > \dfrac{3.5 - 6}{2.05} = P(z > -1.22) = 0.8888$ (Normal)

d. (b) No. $p = 0.30$ is too large. Rule of thumb: $p \leq 0.05$ and $n \geq 20$
(c) Yes. Rule of thumb: $np \geq 5$ and $n(1 - p) \geq 5$

8. a. Assume symmetrical distributions. Therefore, mean equals mode. C has lowest mean productivity. Point C (mean) is lowest (farthest left on X-axis).

b. Employee B has the highest σ. Dispersion around the mean is greatest.

c. Employee A has the lowest coefficient of variation (CV). $CV = \dfrac{\sigma}{\mu}$, A has the smallest numerator (σ) and the largest mean (μ). Both factors lead to a smaller CV.

9. a. $30 = \frac{90 - 70}{10} = 2$; $P(X > 90) = P(z > 2) = 0.5000 - 0.4772 = 0.0228$. The probability distribution for the number of employees with evaluations exceeding 90 is the *binomial distribution* with parameters $\underline{p = 0.0228}$ and $\underline{n = 25}$.

b. $\binom{5}{5}\binom{20}{0}/\binom{25}{5} = 1/\frac{25!}{20!5!} = \boxed{1/53,\ 130} = 0.00002$

10. a. $\overline{X} = \frac{20}{8} = 2\frac{1}{2}$

$$s^2 = \frac{(2-2.5)^2+(3-2.5)^2+(1-2.5)^2+(4-2.5)^2+(2-2.5)^2+(5-2.5)^2+(3-2.5)^2+(0-2.5)^2}{7}$$

$s^2 = 18/7 = 2.57$

$s = \sqrt{2.57} = 1.6$ people

b. Let μ be estimated by $\overline{X} = 2.5$
From Table A-3, interpolate between 2.4 and 2.6
$P(X \geq 4) = 1 - P(X \leq 3) = 1 - 0.757 = 0.243$

11. a. $E(X) = np = 8(.25) = 2$
$E(Y) = (.1)(1) + (.2)(2) + (.3)(3) + (.4)(4) = 3$
$E(X + Y) = 2 + 3 = 5$

b. $P(X \geq 4) = 1 - F(3) = 1 - 0.8862 = 0.1138$ (Table A-1 for $n = 8$, $p = .25$)
$P(Y \geq 4) = 0.4$
$P(X \geq 4 \text{ and } Y \geq 4) = (0.1138)(0.4) = 0.046$

12. a. $Md = 5$ (value of the 100½th item)

b. $\overline{X} = \frac{(1)(6) + (2)(22) + (3)(30) + (4)(35) + (5)(62) + (6)(45)}{200} = 4.3$

$\overline{X} \pm s = 4.3 \pm \sqrt{2} = 4.3 \pm 1.4 = 2.9 \text{ to } 5.7 \approx 3, 4, 5$

30 + 35 + 62 = 127 items. Therefore, 127/200 = 63.5% of the employees fall in the interval.

c. $P(\text{at least one of 5 records scored a "1"}) = 1 - \frac{\binom{6}{0}\binom{22}{5}}{\binom{28}{5}}$

d. *Binomial*
$q = 0.80$ responders
$p = 0.20$ nonresponders $\quad P(X \leq 2 \text{ nonresponders}) = 0.6778$ (Table A-1)
$n = 10$

13. a. $E(X|Y = 5) = (10)(.10/.35) + (20)(.10/.35) + (30)(.15/.35)$
$= 21.4$ units per employee

b. $P(\text{firm produces} < 100 \text{ items per day}) = 0.10$

14. a. $\overline{X} = \frac{0(73) + 1(74) + 2(37) + 3(12) + 4(4)}{200} = 1$

$$s^2 = \frac{0-1)^2(73) + (1-1)^2(74) + (2-1)^2(37) + (3-1)^2(12) + (4-1)^2(4)}{199}$$

$= 0.9749$

b. *Poisson*, because $\overline{X} = s^2$ and $\mu = \sigma^2$ in Poisson

# of units	0	1	2	3	4
Actual	73	74	37	12	4
Theoretical:					
Poisson $\mu = 1$	73.6	73.6	36.8	12.2	3

c. Poisson $\mu = 1$ $F(4) - F(1) = 0.996 - 0.736 = 0.26$
Estimate for number of days = 250(0.26) = 65

15. a. $n = 10$ $p = 0.15$ $1 - F(3) = 1 - 0.95 = 0.05$

b. $n = 5$ $p = 0.05$ $f(2) = F(2) - F(1) = 0.9988 - 0.9774 = 0.0214$

c. $$\frac{\binom{100}{0}\binom{900}{20} + \binom{100}{1}\binom{900}{19}}{\binom{1000}{20}}$$

16. a.

x	$f(x)$	$xf(x)$
0	0.5	0
1	0.2	0.2
2	0.3	0.6
		0.8

y	$f(y)$	$yf(y)$
0	0.45	0
2	0.15	0.3
4	0.40	1.6
		1.9

b. If $X = 1$ we have $P(Y = 0|X = 1) = \frac{1}{4}$; $P(Y = 2|X = 1) = \frac{1}{4}$;
and $P(Y = 4|X = 1) = \frac{1}{2}$

$E(Y|X = 1) = 0(\frac{1}{4}) + 2(\frac{1}{4}) + 4(\frac{1}{2}) = 2\frac{1}{2}$ (million dollars)

If proposal 1 is 1 million dollars than the average net profit from investment proposal 2 is $2\frac{1}{2}$ million dollars.

17. a. $\mu = \dfrac{18 + 16 + 11 + 25 + 10}{5} = 16$ defectives/day $\qquad$ $\text{C.V}_{\text{Dec}} = \dfrac{5.4}{16} = 33.8\%$

$\sigma^2 = \dfrac{(18-16)^2 + (16-16)^2 + (11-16)^2 + (25-16)^2 + (10-16)^2}{5}$ $\qquad$ $\text{C.V}_{\text{Year}} = \dfrac{2}{20} = 10\%$

$\sigma^2 = 2.92 \geq \sigma = \sqrt{29.2} = 5.4$ defectives/day

Since 33.8% > 10%, the *relative variability* of the number of defectives produced during the first week of December is greater than the relative variability for the entire year.

b. $x_1 = 15$; $z_1 = \dfrac{15 - 20}{2} = -2.5$; $A_1 = 0.4938$

$x_2 = 21$; $z_2 = \dfrac{21 - 20}{2} = 0.5$; $A_2 = 0.1915$

$P(15 \leq x \leq 21) = P(-2.5 < z < 0.5) = 0.4938 + 0.1915 = 0.6853$

c. $\sigma_{\overline{x}} = \dfrac{2}{\sqrt{5}} = 0.8944$

$\overline{x}_0 = 18$; $z = \dfrac{18 - 20}{0.8944} = -2.24$

$P(\overline{x} < 18) = P(z < -2.24) = 0.5000 - 0.4875 = 0.0125$

d. $z = \dfrac{2}{2/\sqrt{5}} = 2.24$

$P(|\overline{x} - \mu| > 2.24) = 1 - 2(.4875) = 0.0250$

18. a. *Poisson Distribution* (Table A-3)

$\mu = 2$; $P(X = 2) = 0.677 - 0.406 = 0.271$
$\mu = 4$; $P(X = 3) = 0.433 - 0.238 = 0.195$
P(pattern: 2, 2, 3) = (0.271)(0.271)(0.195) = 0.0143

b. *Poisson Distribution* (Table A-3)

$\mu = 6$ calls/2 hour period
$P(4 \le x \le 6) = F(6) - F(3) = 0.606 - 0.151 = 0.455$

c. *Poisson Distribution* (Table A-3)

$\mu = 4$ calls
$P(X \ge 3) = 1 - F(2) = 1 - 0.238 = 0.762$

Binomial Distribution

$P(X = 4 \text{ successes}) = \binom{5}{4}(.24)^1(.76)^4 = 0.4003$

Alternatively, let $p = 0.75$, $n = 5$

Since P(4 successes) = P(1 failure), then using $p = 0.25$, $n = 5$ and Table A-2

$P(X = 1) = 0.3955 \approx 0.40$

19. a. $P\left(\frac{X}{Y} > .6\right) = .2 + .4 + .1 + .1 = 0.8$

There is an 80% probability that the monthly quantity demanded will exceed 0.6 of the monthly quantity supplied. Alternatively, there is an 80% probability that the ratio of monthly quantity demanded to monthly quantity supplied will exceed 0.6.

b. $E(Z) = E(Y) - E(X) = 1.4 - 1.4 = 0$

The expected value of the monthly quantity supplied minus the expected value of the monthly quantity demanded equals zero. That is, on the average, there is no monthly surplus nor monthly shortage.

CHAPTER 6

Exercises 6.2

1. a. Interval estimate.
   b. Estimator.
   c. Point estimate.
   d. Interval estimate.

2. a. See the discussion in section 6.2.

3. a. False. Unbiasedness is only one criterion of goodness of estimation. The "best" estimator is the unbiased estimator with the smallest variance.
   b. False.
   c. False. If two competing estimators are both *un*biased, then the one with the smallest variance (for a given sample size) is relatively more efficient.

4. Part (c) is best since (a) is a single point estimate which can be either right or wrong. As for (b), despite the perfect forecast, the range of estimate is too wide and, hence, useless.

5. The larger the sample size, the greater is the cost of sampling. Therefore, most practical estimation situations involve trade-offs between precision and cost.

Exercises 6.3

1. Because $\bar{x}$ can take on different values depending on which sample is drawn from a population with mean μ, $\bar{x}$ is a random variable. As such, it has a probability distribution, and the standard deviation of $\bar{x}$ is a measure of the dispersion of that probability distribution. This standard deviation is a measure of the spread of $\bar{x}$ values around μ, the value to be estimated. Therefore, it can be interpreted as a measure of errors due to sampling. From this viewpoint, $\sigma_{\bar{x}}$ is a measure of the error involved in using $\bar{x}$ as an estimator of μ.

2. a. $5.2 \pm 2.00(0.9/\sqrt{36})$, or 4.90 - 5.50 flavors

   b. In repeated samples randomly drawn from the population, 95.5% of the intervals as drawn in part a would include the population mean.

3. No. $105 \pm 1.96(50/\sqrt{400})$, or a ratings range of 100.1 - 109.9

4. $50 \pm 2.17(15/\sqrt{400})$, or 48.37 - 51.63 minutes

5. $1.2 \pm (1.96)\sqrt{\frac{5{,}000 - 100}{5{,}000 - 1}}\left(\frac{0.9}{\sqrt{100}}\right)$, or 1.025 - 1.375

6. No. From the viewpoint of classical statistics, it is incorrect to make probability statements about population parameters.

7. $0.59 \pm 2\sqrt{(0.59)(0.41)/100}$, or 0.492 - 0.688 favored a new bond issue.

8. $1.9 \pm 1.65(1.0/\sqrt{100})$, or 1.735 - 2.065

9. $\overline{X} = \dfrac{\Sigma X}{n} = \$12.15$

   The 99% confidence interval is $\$12.15 \pm 2.575(\$.20/\sqrt{8})$ or \$11.97 - \$12.33.

10. a. $150 \pm 2(40/\sqrt{100}) = 150 \pm 8$, or 142 - 158 gallons

    b. Accept a lower level of confidence or increase the sample size.

11. a. $10.1\% \pm (2.575)\sqrt{\dfrac{10,000 - 100}{10,000 - 1}}\left(\dfrac{2.5\%}{\sqrt{100}}\right)$

    $10.1\% \pm 0.64\%$, or 9.46 - 10.74%

    b. In repeated samples randomly drawn from the population of lamp manufacturers, 99% of the intervals constructed as in part a would include the true population mean.

12. a. $232 \pm 2.00(40/\sqrt{400})$, or from 228 to 236 employees

    b. In repeated samples randomly drawn from the same population, 95.5% of the intervals constructed as in (a) would include the true population mean.

13. No. From the viewpoint of classical statistics, it is incorrect to make probability statements about population parameters.

14. a. $0.60 \pm 1.65\sqrt{(0.6)(0.4)/400}$, or from 0.560 to 0.640 preferred sales help

    b. $(0.30 - 0.27) \pm (1.96)\sqrt{\dfrac{(0.30)(0.70)}{100} + \dfrac{(0.27)(0.73)}{300}}$,

    or from -0.073 to 0.133. In all possible pairs of samples drawn from the same population, 95% of the confidence intervals established by this method would contain the actual difference between the population proportions.

15. a. $\$23.50 \pm 2.58(\$6.00/\sqrt{100})$, or from \$21.95 to \$25.05. Note that the finite population correction is equal to $\sqrt{(10,000 - 100)/(10,000 - 1)}$. Since the finite population correction is approximately equal to 1, it has not been included in the calculation of the standard error of the mean.

    b. Note that the finite population correction is equal to $\sqrt{(10,000 - 100)/(10,000 - 1)} = 0.995 \approx 1$.

    Since the finite population correction is approximately equal to 1, it has not been included in the calculation of the standard error of the mean.

Exercises 6.4

1. a. True, where $s_{\overline{x}} = s/\sqrt{n}$ and $s = \sqrt{\Sigma(x - x)^2/(n-1)}$. The t value is determined for $\upsilon = n - 1$ degrees of freedom.

   b. True. If the statistics are unbiased, then the more efficient statistic has a smaller standard error.

c. False. The 95% confidence interval means that 95% of all possible samples would yield intervals including the true population mean strength of this type of wood beam. A confidence interval does not refer to a range of values within any particular sample.

2. a. $73 \pm 3.355(11.18/\sqrt{9}) = 73 \pm 12.50$, or 60.50 - 85.50

b. We assume in the derivation of the t distribution that the underlying population is normally distributed. This assumption would be violated by a highly skewed population distribution. Hence, the range set up in part a would not have exactly a 99% confidence coefficient associated with it.

3. a. $3 \pm 2.145(1/\sqrt{15})$, or 2.45 - 3.55
$t = 2.145$ for $\upsilon = 14$ and a 0.95 confidence coefficient)

b. As stated in the solution to exercise 1c above, 95% confidence refers to the percentage of all possible samples that would result in intervals containing the true population mean. Since the university has already drawn a sample, the interval estimate is either correct (one of the 95%) or incorrect (one of the 5%).

4. a. $\$.60 \pm 2.861(\$.15/\sqrt{20}) = \$.60 \pm \$.096$, or \$.504 - \$.696

b. For a 90% confidence coefficient

$\$.60 \pm 1.729(\$.15/\sqrt{20}) = \$.60 \pm \$.058$, or \$.542 - \$.658

For a 95% confidence coefficient

$\$.60 \pm 2.093(\$.15/\sqrt{20}) = \$.60 \pm 0.07$, or \$.53 - \$.67

5. a. $\$600{,}000 \pm 2.602(\$20{,}000/\sqrt{16}) = \$600{,}000 \pm \$13{,}010$,
or from \$586,990 to \$613,010
($t = 2.602$ for $\nu = 15$ and 0.98 confidence coefficient).

b. A higher level of confidence would increase the width of the interval. A larger sample would decrease the width of the interval.

6. a. $51 \pm 3.355(16.10/\sqrt{9}) = 51 \pm 18.02$, or from 32.98 minutesto 69.02 minutes.

b. It is assumed in the derivation of the t distribution that the underlying population is normally distributed, and this assumption would be violated by a highly skewed population distribution. Hence, the range set up in part (a) would not have exactly a 99% confidence coefficient associated with it.

Exercises 6.5

1. $2.055\sigma_{\bar{p}} = 0.04$

$$\frac{0.04}{2.055} = \sqrt{\frac{(0.5)(0.5)}{n}}$$

$$n = 659.8$$

Therefore, the necessary sample size is 660.

2. a. $0.56 \pm (2.33)\sqrt{(0.56)(0.44)/100}$, or 0.444 - 0.676 of the time

b. $2.33\sigma_{\bar{p}} = 0.03$

$$\frac{0.03}{2.33} = \sqrt{\frac{(0.5)(0.5)}{n}}$$

$$n = 1{,}508.0$$

Therefore, the necessary sample size is 1,508.

3. a. $1.96\sigma_{\bar{p}} = 0.03$

$$\frac{0.03}{1.96} = \sqrt{\frac{(0.2)(0.8)}{n}}$$

$n = 682.95$

Therefore, the necessary sample size is 683.

b. $0.15 \pm (2.575)\sqrt{\frac{(0.15)(0.85)}{100}} = 0.15 \pm 0.092$, or $0.058 - 0.242$

4. a. Of all possible samples he could draw, 95.5% will yield a correct interval estimate, whereas 4.5% of all possible samples will lead to an incorrect interval estimate.

b. $2(55{,}840/\sqrt{n}) = 5{,}000;\ n \approx 499$

5. $1.96\sigma_{\bar{p}} = 0.03$

$$\frac{0.03}{1.96} = \sqrt{\frac{(0.25)(0.75)}{n}}$$

$n = 800.3$

Therefore, the necessary sample size is 801.

6. The cost of taking a larger sample might be uneconomical when compared with the return on the sample information.

7. a. $0.89 \pm 2.575\sqrt{\frac{(0.11)(0.89)}{100}} = 0.89 \pm 0.081$, or $0.809 - 0.971$

b. $1.96\sigma_{\bar{p}} = 0.05$

$$\frac{0.05}{1.96} = \sqrt{\frac{(0.5)(0.5)}{n}}$$

$n = 384.16$

Therefore, the necessary sample size is 385.

8. $2(\$.05/\sqrt{n}) = \$0.005$

$n = 400$

9. a. $0.60 \pm 1.645\sqrt{\frac{(0.6)(0.4)}{100}} = 0.60 \pm 0.081$, or $0.519 - 0.681$

b. $2.575\sigma_{\bar{p}} = 0.05$

$$\frac{0.05}{2.575} = \sqrt{\frac{(0.5)(0.5)}{n}}$$

$n = 663.1$

Therefore, the necessary sample size is 664.

10. a. 95.5% of all the possible samples he could draw will yield a correct interval estimate, whereas 4.5% of all possible samples will lead to an incorrect interval estimate.

b. $2(\$0.50/\sqrt{n}) = \$.05;\ n = 400$

11. $(2.33)\sqrt{(0.05)(0.95)/n} = 0.005$

$n = 10{,}326$

CHAPTER 7

Exercises 7.2

1. A parameter is a measure computed from a population, whereas a statistic is a measure computed from a sample. Hence a statistic takes on various possible values depending upon which sample is drawn.

2. The statement is incorrect, since there are two types of errors that can occur, Type I and Type II. If α (the probability of a Type I error) is made extremely small, the Type II error probability (with a fixed sample size) will tend to become quite large. The two errors, for a fixed sample size, move inversely to one another. As an extreme case, for example, if we always accept H_0 regardless of test results, the α error is 0, but the β error is equal to 1.

3. a. Procedurally, in a one-tailed test, rejection of the null hypothesis takes place in only one tail of the sampling distribution. In a two-tailed test, rejection of the null hypothesis takes place in both tails of the distribution.
   b. Type I error is the error of rejecting H_0 when in fact H_0 is true.

4. Power is defined as the probability of rejecting H_0 when H_1 is the true state of nature. Power = $1 - \beta$.

5. a. P(Type I error) $= P(\bar{p} > 0.55 | p = 0.5)$

$$= P\left(z > \frac{0.55 - 0.50}{\sqrt{(0.5)(0.5)/300}}\right) = 0.0418$$

   b. H_0: $p \le 0.5$
   H_1: $p > 0.5$
   $\alpha = 0.01$

   Critical value $= 0.5 + (2.33)\sqrt{\frac{(0.5)(0.5)}{300}}$
   $= 0.5 + 0.067$
   $= 0.567$

   Decision Rule

   1. Reject H_0 if $\bar{p} > 0.567$
   2. Do not reject H_0 otherwise

   Reject H_0, since $\bar{p} = \frac{180}{130} = 0.600 > 0.567$.

   c. Use the test in part (a), because for a fixed n, the higher the Type I error level, the lower the Type II error level.

6. a. H_0: $\mu \le 250$
H_1: $\mu > 250$
$\alpha = 0.01$
Critical value = $250 + 2.33(40/\sqrt{200}) = 257$

Decision Rule

1. Reject H_0 if $\bar{x} > 257$ and widen the bridge
2. Do not reject H_0 otherwise

b. $z = \dfrac{(255 - 250)}{40/\sqrt{200}} = 1.77$

p value = $P(z > 1.77) = 0.5000 - 0.4616 = 0.0384$

7. a. H_0: $\mu = 12$
H_1: $\mu < 12$
$\alpha = 0.05$
Critical value = $12 - 1.65(2/\sqrt{80}) = 11.63$

Decision Rule

1. Reject H_0 if $\bar{x} < 11.63$
2. Do not reject H_0 otherwise

Reject H_0. Conclude that the morale improvement plan decreases the absenteeism rate.

b. $z = \dfrac{11.5 - 12}{2/\sqrt{80}} = -2.24$

p value = $P(z < -2.24) = 0.5000 - 0.4875 = 0.0125$

8. a. H_0: $\mu \le 0.012$
H_1: $\mu > 0.012$

Critical value = $0.012 + 2.33(0.002/\sqrt{50}) = 0.0127$

Decision Rule

1. Reject H_0 if $\bar{x} > 0.0127$
2. Do not reject H_0 otherwise

Since $\bar{x} = 0.015 > 0.0127$, we reject H_0.

We would conclude that the average mortality rate in these cities is above the national rate.

b. $z = \dfrac{0.015 - 0.012}{0.002/\sqrt{50}} = 10.6$

p value = 0.0000

9. H_0: $\mu = 4$ ounces
H_1: $\mu < 4$ ounces
$\alpha = 0.005$

Critical value = $4 - 1.65(0.9/\sqrt{400}) = 3.93$ ounces

Decision Rule

1. Reject H_0 (accuse restaurant) if $\bar{x} < 3.93$
2. Do not reject H_0 (do not accuse restaurant) otherwise

10. H_0: $\mu = 8.0\%$
    H_1: $\mu \neq 8.0\%$

    Critical value = $8\% \pm 1.96(0.3/\sqrt{200})$, or 7.9584% and 8.0416%

    Decision Rule

    1. Reject H_0 if $7.9584\% > \bar{x}$ or $\bar{x} > 8.0416\%$
    2. Do not reject H_0 if $7.9584\% < \bar{x} < 8.0416\%$

    a. No. We would not be willing to conclude that a change had taken place. Because $\bar{x} = 8.03\%$ does not fall in the rejection region, we cannot reject H_0: $\mu = 8.0\%$

    b. $P(\text{Type II error}) = P(-3.00 < z < 1.02) = 0.8448$

    c. The probability is 0.8448 of concluding that the arithmetic mean interest rate has not changed from 8.0%, when in fact two years later it was 8.02%.
    Note: This is a tricky problem. Students are tempted to treat it as a case of hypothesis testing concerning a proportion rather than a mean.

11. a. H_0: $\mu \le 30$ miles per gallon
       H_1: $\mu > 30$ miles per gallon
       $\alpha = 0.02$

    Critical value = $30 + 2.05(4/\sqrt{100}) = 30 + 0.83 = 30.82$

    Decision Rule

    1. Reject H_0 if $\bar{x} > 30.82$
    2. Do not reject H_0 if $\bar{x} \le 30.82$

    b. (1) $$P(\bar{x} < 30.82 \mid \mu = 32) = P\left(z \le \frac{30.82 - 32}{4/\sqrt{100}}\right) = P(z \le -2.95) = 0.0016$$

    (2) Incorrectly retaining the null hypothesis is a Type II error.

12. Probability of Type I error = $P(\bar{p} \le 0.25 \mid p = 0.30)$

    $$P\left(z \le \frac{0.25 - 0.30}{\sqrt{(0.3)(0.7)/300}}\right)$$

    $$P(z \le -1.89) = 0.0294$$

    The Type I error here is an incorrect decision to discontinue the program.

13. a. $$P(\text{retaining } H_0 \mid \mu = 71) = P\left(\frac{68.04 - 71}{1} < z < \frac{71.96 - 71}{1}\right) = 0.830$$

    b. The power of the test when $\mu = 71$ is the probability of rejecting the null hypothesis, H_0: $\mu = 70$, for $\mu = 71$. The power for $\mu = 71$ is $1 - \beta = 1 - 0.830 = 0.170$.

    c. $1.96 = z(10/\sqrt{100})$
       $z = 1.96$
       $\alpha = 0.05$ level of significance

14. H_0: $p \geq 0.06$
H_1: $p < 0.06$
$\alpha = 0.05$

Critical value = $0.06 - 1.65\sqrt{(0.06)(0.94)/1{,}000} = 0.048$

Decision Rule

1. Reject H_0 if $\bar{p} < 0.048$
2. Do not reject H_0 otherwise

Reject H_0, since $0.038 < 0.048$ and decide that the system is effective.

15. H_0: $\mu = 240$
H_1: $\mu > 240$
$\alpha = 0.05$

Critical value = $240 + 1.65(25/\sqrt{30}) = 247.5$

Decision Rule

1. Reject H_0 if $\bar{x} > 247.5$
2. Do not reject H_0 if $\bar{x} \leq 247.5$

Because $\bar{x} = 245 < 247.5$, we cannot reject H_0 and therefore cannot conclude that the extended coffee breaks have increased worker productivity.

16. a. H_0: $p = 0.35$
H_1: $p \neq 0.35$
$\alpha = 0.02$

Critical value = $= 0.35 \pm (2.33)\sqrt{(0.35)(0.65)/600}$
$= 0.35 \pm 0.045$ or 0.305 and 0.395

Decision Rule

1. Reject H_0 if $\bar{p} < 0.305$ or $\bar{p} > 0.395$
2. Do not reject H_0 if $0.305 \leq \bar{p} \leq 0.395$

Reject H_0, because $\bar{p} = (175/600) = 0.292 < 0.305$. The J.T. McClay Company should alter its marketing campaign.

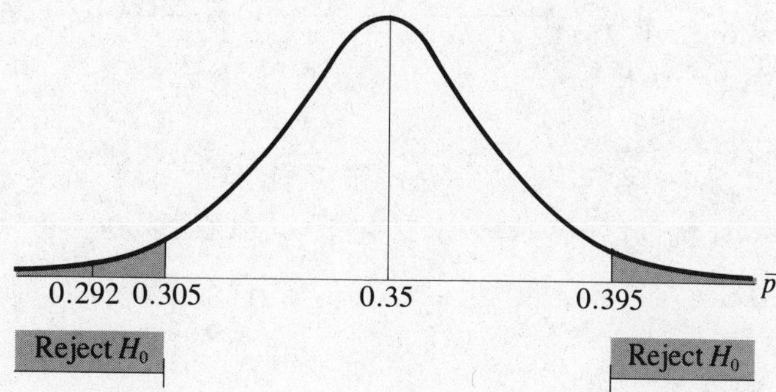

b. H_0: $p \geq 0.35$
H_1: $p < 0.35$
$\alpha = 0.02$

Critical value $= 0.35 - 2.05\sqrt{(0.35)(0.65)/600}$
$= 0.35 - 0.040$
$= 0.31$

Decision Rule

1. Reject H_0 if $\bar{p} < 0.31$
2. Do not reject H_0 if $\bar{p} \geq 0.31$

Reject H_0, since $\bar{p} = (175/600) = 0.292 < 0.31$.

17. H_0: $p \geq 0.667$
H_1: $p < 0.667$
$\alpha = 0.05$

Critical value $= 0.667 - (1.65)\sqrt{\frac{(0.667)(0.333)}{85}}\sqrt{\frac{435-85}{435-1}}$
$= 0.667 - 0.076 = 0.591$

Decision Rule

1. Reject H_0 if $\bar{p} < 0.591$
2. Do not reject H_0 otherwise

Retain H_0, because $\bar{p} = (52/85) = 0.612 > 0.591$.
You cannot conclude that the veto will not be overridden.

Exercises 7.3

1. a. (5) c. (2)
   b. (1) d. (4)

2. H_0: $\mu_1 = \mu_2$ (The two countries have the same mean height.)
H_1: $\mu_1 \neq \mu_2$ (The two countries have different mean heights.)
$\alpha = 0.05$

Critical value $= 0 \pm (1.96)\sqrt{(3)^2/2,000 + (2)^2/1,500}$
$= 0 \pm 0.166$

Decision Rule

1. Reject H_0 if $\bar{x}_1 - \bar{x}_2 < -0.166$ or $\bar{x}_1 - \bar{x}_2 > 0.166$
2. Do not reject H_0 if $-0.166 \leq \bar{x}_1 - \bar{x}_2 \leq 0.166$.

Reject H_0 since $69.1 - 68.3 = 0.8 > 0.166$

3. a. H_0: $\mu_1 = \mu_2$
H_1: $\mu_1 \neq \mu_2$
$\alpha = 0.02$

Critical value $= 0 \pm (2.33)\sqrt{(150)^2/150 + (130)^2/200}$
$= 0 \pm 35.68$

Decision Rule

1. Reject H_0 if $\bar{x}_1 - \bar{x}_2 < -35.68$ or $\bar{x}_1 - \bar{x}_2 > 35.68$
2. Do not reject H_0 if $-35.68 \leq \bar{x}_1 - \bar{x}_2 \leq 35.68$

Reject H_0, since 2,000 - 1,960 = 40 > 35.68.

$$z = \frac{2,000 - 1,960}{\sqrt{\frac{(150)^2}{150} + \frac{(130)^2}{200}}} = 2.61$$

p value = $P(z > 2.61)$ = 0.5000 - 0.4955 = 0.0045

See figure.

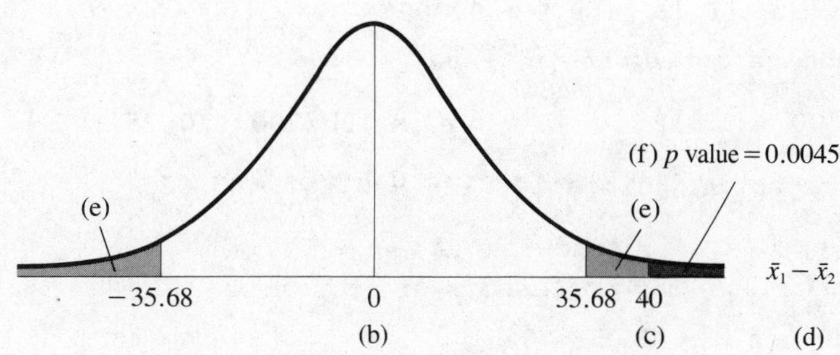

Figure for exercise 3(b-f)

4. Because a census was conducted (and assuming the data are accurate), we can conclude that the average balance due on customers' accounts at Bombergers exceeds that due on the accounts at Zimbels. Testing a hypothesis to draw an inference about the population means would be a waste. We already know that the population mean of $56 is greater than the population mean of $38.

5. H_0: $\mu_1 = \mu_2$
   H_1: $\mu_1 \neq \mu_2$
   $\alpha = 0.05$

   Critical value = $= 0 \pm (1.96)\sqrt{(1.5)^2/60 + (0.8)^2/60}$
   $= 0 \pm 0.43$

   Decision Rule

   1. Reject H_0 if $\bar{x}_1 - \bar{x}_2 < -0.43$ or $\bar{x}. - \bar{x}_2 > 0.43$
   2. Do not reject H_0 if $-0.43 \leq \bar{x}_1 - \bar{x}_2 \leq 0.43$

   Reject H_0, since 7.5 - 6.6 = 0.90 > 0.43, and conclude that the trained and untrained salespeople do not have equivalent average mean performance ratings.

6. H_0: $p_A = p_B$
   H_1: $p_A \neq p_B$
   $\alpha = 0.01$
   $\bar{p} = (72 + 84)/(100 + 100) = 0.78$

   Critical value = $= 0 \pm (2.57)\sqrt{(0.78)(0.22)(1/100 + 1/100)}$
   $= 0 \pm 0.15$

   Decision Rule

   1. Reject H_0 if $|\bar{p}_A - \bar{p}_B| > 0.15$
   2. Do not reject H_0 if $|\bar{p}_A - \bar{p}_B| \leq 0.15$

   Do not reject H_0, since $|0.72 - 0.84| < 0.15$.

   Therefore, we cannot conclude that the two groups differed with respect to whether they would purchase the cookies tasted.

7. H_0: $p_A = p_B$
   H_1: $p_A \neq p_B$
   $\alpha = 0.05$
   $\overline{p} = 475/600 = 0.792$
   Critical value = $= 0 \pm (1.96)\sqrt{(0.792)(0.208)(1/400 + 1/200)}$
   $= 0 \pm 0.069$

   Decision Rule

   1. Reject H_0 if $|\overline{p}_A - \overline{p}_B| > 0.069$
   2. Do not reject H_0 if $|\overline{p}_A - \overline{p}_B| \leq 0.069$

   $\overline{p}_A = 325/400 = 0.8125$ $\qquad$ $\overline{p}_B = 150/200 = 0.75$

   Do not reject H_0, since $|0.8125 - 0.75| < 0.069$

8. a. H_0: $p_T = p_{PE}$ $\quad$ T = traders
   H_1: $p_T \neq p_{PE}$ $\quad$ PE = professors of economics
   Assume that $\alpha = 0.05$

   $$\overline{p} = \frac{135 + 154}{225 + 200} = \frac{289}{425} = 0.68$$

   $$\text{Critical value} = 0 \pm (1.96)\sqrt{(0.68)(0.32)\left(\frac{1}{200} + \frac{1}{225}\right)}$$
   $$= 0 \pm 1.96(0.045) = 0 \pm 0.088$$

   Decision Rule

   1. Reject H_0 if $|\overline{p}_T - \overline{p}_{PE}| > 0.088$
   2. Do not reject H_0 if $|\overline{p}_T - \overline{p}_{PE}| \leq 0.088$

   $$\overline{p}_T = \frac{135}{225} = 0.60, \quad \overline{p}_{PE} = \frac{154}{200} = 0.77$$

   Decision: Reject H_0, since $|\overline{p}_T - \overline{p}_{PE}| = |0.6 - 0.77| = 0.17 > 0.088$

   b. The error of concluding that there is a difference in the proportions of foreign exchange traders and professors of economics who believe that flexible exchange rates will enhance international monetary stability, when in fact the proportions are the same.

9. a. H_0: $p_A = p_B$ $\quad$ or $\quad$ H_0: $p_A - p_B = 0$
   H_1: $p_A \neq p_B$ $\quad\quad\quad$ H_1: $p_A - p_B \neq 0$
   Assume that $\alpha = 0.01$
   $\overline{p} = (200 + 60)/(400 + 100) = 260/500 = 0.52$

   $$\text{Critical value} = 0 \pm (2.57)\sqrt{(0.52)(0.48)\left(\frac{1}{400} + \frac{1}{100}\right)}$$
   $$= 0 \pm 2.57(0.056) = 0 \pm 0.144$$

   Decision Rule

   1. Reject H_0 if $|\overline{p}_A - \overline{p}_B| > 0.144$
   2. Do not reject H_0 if $|\overline{p}_A - \overline{p}_B| \leq 0.144$

   $$\overline{p}_A = \frac{200}{400} = 0.5; \quad \overline{p}_B = \frac{60}{100} = 0.6$$

   Decision: Do not reject H_0, since $|\overline{p}_A - \overline{p}_B| = |0.5 - 0.6| = 0.1 < 0.144$

The sample proportions $\bar{p}_A - \bar{p}_B$ did not differ significantly; therefore, we cannot conclude that the two groups of workers differed with respect to their opinions on the most important labor-management problem in their industries.

b. See figure.

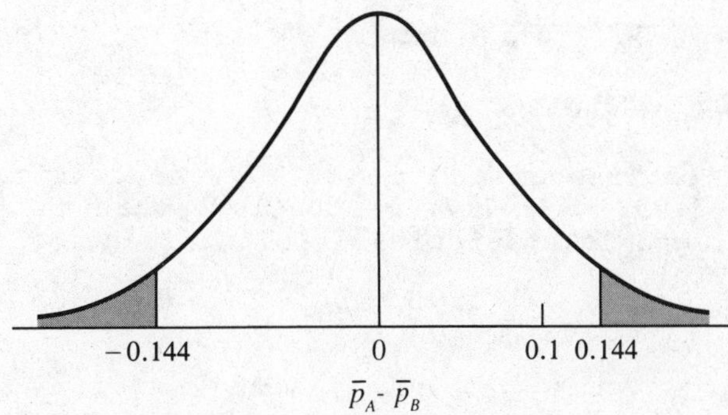

Figure for exercise 9(b)

10. H_0: $p_1 = p_2$

H_1: $p_1 \neq p_2$

$\alpha = 0.05$

$\bar{p} = 398/900 = 0.442$

Critical value $0 \pm (1.96)\sqrt{(0.442)(0.558)\left(\frac{1}{400} + \frac{1}{500}\right)} = \pm 0.065$

Decision Rule

1. Reject H_0 if $|\bar{p}_1 - \bar{p}_2| > 0.065$
2. Do not reject H_0 if $|\bar{p}_1 - \bar{p}_2| \leq 0.065$

Decision: Do not reject H_0, since $|0.47 - 0.42| < 0.065$

Exercises 7.4

1. a. H_0: $\mu = 2.80$

H_1: $\mu \neq 2.80$

$\alpha = 0.05$

$s_{\bar{x}} = 0.35/\sqrt{10} = 0.11$

$$t = \frac{(3.00 - 2.80)}{0.11} = 1.82$$

For 10 − 1 = 9 degrees of freedom, the critical value of t is 2.26. Since 1.82 < 2.26, we cannot reject H_0, we conclude that these data are consistent with a claim that the mean grade point average in this university is 2.80.

b. $s_{\bar{x}} = 0.35/\sqrt{100} = 0.035$

$$t = \frac{(3.00 - 2.80)}{0.035} = 5.71$$

For 100 − 1 = 99 degrees of freedom and $\alpha = 0.05$, the critical value of $t \approx 1.98$. Since 5.71 > 1.98, we reject H_0.

c. These results indicate that the statistical significance of a difference between a statistic and a parameter depends on the size of the sample in which the statistic is observed. Of course, with a sample size of 100, we could have used the normal curve test in part b. We would have reached the same conclusion.

2. a. $\hat{s}^2 = \dfrac{13(0.25)^2 + 9(0.10)^2}{14 + 10 - 2} = 0.041$

$s_{\bar{x}_1-\bar{x}_2} = \sqrt{0.041}\sqrt{1/14 + 1/10} = 0.084$

$t = \dfrac{\$1.22 - \$1.48}{0.084} = -3.095$

For 22 degrees of freedom and $\alpha = 0.10$, the critical value of t is -1.717. Since $-3.095 < -1.717$, we conclude that the difference between the sample averages is statistically significant.

b. H_0: $\mu_1 - \mu_2 = 0$
H_1: $\mu_1 - \mu_2 \neq 0$

Decision Rule

1. Reject H_0 if $t < -1.717$ or $t > 1.717$
2. Do not reject H_0 if $-1.717 \leq t \leq 1.717$

3. $\bar{x} = 1190 \qquad s = \sqrt{\dfrac{\Sigma(x-\bar{x})^2}{n-1}} = \sqrt{\dfrac{4,600}{9}} = 22.6;\ n = 10$

H_0: $\mu \leq 1,200$
H_1: $\mu > 1,200$

For $10 - 1 = 9$ degrees of freedom, the critical value of t in a one-tailed test is 2.821.

Decision Rule

1. Reject H_0 if $t > 2.821$
2. Accept H_0 otherwise

$s_{\bar{x}} = 22.6/\sqrt{10} = 7.147 \qquad t = (1,190 - 1,200)/7.147 = -1.399$

Since $-1.399 < 2.821$, we accept H_0 and conclude that the sample average is consistent with the hypothesis that 1,200 cars or fewer pass this site each day. Hence, the owner's claim is not substantiated.

4.

Brand A	Brand B
$\bar{x}_A = 22$	$\bar{x}_B = 20$
$s_A = 4.77$	$s_B = 3.42$
$n_A = 15$	$n_B = 15$

H_0: $\mu_A = \mu_B$
H_1: $\mu_A \neq \mu_B$

For 28 degrees of freedom and $\alpha = 0.05$, the critical value of t is 2.048.

Decision Rule

1. Reject H_0 if $t < -2.048$ or $t > 2.048$
2. Do not reject H_0 if $-2.048 \leq t \leq 2.048$

$s_A = \sqrt{318/14} = 4.77$

$s_B = \sqrt{164/14} = 3.42$

$$\hat{s}^2 = \frac{14(4.77)^2 + 14(3.42)^2}{15 + 15 - 2} = 17.22$$

$s_{\bar{X}_A - \bar{X}_B} = \sqrt{17.22}\,(\sqrt{1/15 + 1/15}) = 1.52$

$t = (22 - 20)/1.52 = 1.32$

Since $-2.048 \le 1.32 \le 2.048$, we cannot conclude that there was a statistically significant difference between the sample means.

5. a. $$s^2 = \frac{14(10)^2 + 10(12)^2}{15 + 11 - 2} = 118.33$$

$$s_{\bar{x}_1 - \bar{x}_2} = \sqrt{118.33}\left(\sqrt{\frac{1}{15} + \frac{1}{11}}\right) = 10.878(0.397) = 4.32$$

$$t = \frac{60 - 55}{4.32} = 1.16$$

For 24 degrees of freedom and $\alpha = 0.10$, the critical value of t is equal to 1.711. Since $1.16 < 1.711$, we conclude that there was not a statistically significant difference between the sample averages.

b. H_0: $\mu_1 - \mu_2 = 0$
H_1: $\mu_1 - \mu_2 \neq 0$

Decision Rule

1. Reject H_0 if $t < -1.711$ or $t > 1.711$
2. Do not reject H_0 if $-1.711 \le t \le 1.711$

6. H_0: $\mu_1 - \mu_2 = 0$
H_1: $\mu_1 - \mu_2 \neq 0$
$\alpha = 0.02$

$$\hat{s}^2 = \frac{(14)(0.05)^2 + (12)(0.03)^2}{15 + 13 - 2} = 0.001762$$

$$s_{\bar{X}_1 - \bar{X}_2} = \sqrt{0.001762}\left(\sqrt{\frac{1}{15} + \frac{1}{13}}\right) = 0.016$$

Critical values = $0 \pm (2.479)(0.016) = \pm 0.040$

Decision Rule

1. Retain H_0 if $-0.040 \le \bar{x}_1 - \bar{x}_2| \le 0.040$
2. Otherwise, reject H_0.

Since $0.02 < 0.040$, we retain H_0. The assistant cannot conclude that there is a significant difference between the sample average success rates of the two investment banking firms.

7. H_0: $\mu_1 - \mu_2 \le 0$
H_1: $\mu_1 - \mu_2 > 0$
$\alpha = 0.01$

$$\hat{s}^2 = \frac{9(4)^2 + 9(5)^2}{10 + 10 - 2} = 20.5$$

$$s_{\bar{X}_1 - \bar{X}_2} = \hat{s}\sqrt{\frac{1}{10} + \frac{1}{10}} = \sqrt{20.5}\sqrt{\frac{1}{10} + \frac{1}{10}} = 2.025$$

Critical value = $0 + (2.878)(2.025) = 5.828$

Decision Rule

1. Retain H_0 if $|\bar{x}_1 - \bar{x}_2| \le 5.828$.
2. Otherwise, reject H_0.

Since 4 < 5.828, we retain H_0 and conclude that the mean production rate with the bonus plan does not exceed that without the plan.

Exercises 7.5

1. $n = \left[\frac{(2.33 + 1.65)10}{(50 - 47)}\right]^2 \approx 176$

Decision Rule

1. If $\bar{x} < 48.2$ hours, reject the shipment
2. If $\bar{x} \ge 48.2$ hours, accept the shipment

2. $n = \left[\frac{(1.65 + 2.33)\$9}{(30 - \$28)}\right]^2 \approx 321$

Decision Rule

1. If $\bar{x} < \$29.17$, reject H_0: $\mu = \$30$
2. If $\bar{x} \ge \$29.17$, retain H_0: $\mu = \$30$

3. $n = \left[\frac{(1.88 + 2.05)8}{(50 - 54)}\right]^2 \approx 62$

Decision Rule

1. If $\bar{x} \le 51.9$, retain H_0
2. If $\bar{x} > 51.9$, reject H_0

Exercises 7.6

1. Let μ_w and μ_{wo} be the mean population reaction times with medication and without medication, respectively.

H_0: $\mu_w = \mu_{wo}$

H_1: $\mu_w > \mu_{wo}$

$\alpha = 0.05$

$s_{\bar{d}} = 0.0806/\sqrt{12} = 0.0233$

The critical value of t is 1.796 for $\nu = 11$ in a one-tailed test.

Decision Rule

1. Reject H_0 if $t > 1.796$
2. Do not reject H_0 otherwise

Since $t = 0.04/0.0233 = 1.72 < 1.796$, we accept H_0. We cannot conclude that the medication increases reaction time.

2. Let μ_A and μ_B be the mean population comprehension ratings after and before the course, respectively.

H_0: $\mu_A = \mu_B$

H_1: $\mu_A > \mu_B$

$s_{\bar{d}} = 0.455/\sqrt{13} = 0.216$

The critical value of t is 1.782 for $\nu = 12$ in a one-tailed test.

Decision Rule

1. Reject H_0 if $t > 1.782$
2. Do not reject H_0 otherwise

Since $t = 0.04/0.126 = 3.175 > 1.782$, reject H_0 and conclude that the Blair Good Reading Comprehension Course is effective in increasing reading comprehension ratings.

3. a. Let μ_A and μ_B represent the mean population ratings for concern for production after and before the session, respectively.

H_0: $\mu_A = \mu_B$

H_1: $\mu_A > \mu_B$

$s_{\bar{d}} = 1.84/\sqrt{11} = 0.55$

The critical value of t is 2.228 for $\nu = 10$ in a one-tailed test.

Decision Rule

1. Reject H_0 if $t > 2.228$
2. Do not reject H_0 otherwise

Since $t = 1/0.55 = 1.82 < 2.228$, we cannot reject H_0. We conclude that the session does not have a positive effect on managerial ratings for production concern.

b. Let μ_A and μ_B be the mean population ratings for concern for people after and before the session, respectively.

H_0: $\mu_A = \mu_B$

H_1: $\mu_A > \mu_B$

$s_{\bar{d}} = 1.18/\sqrt{11} = 0.36$

Since $t = 1/0.36 = 2.78 > 2.228$, we reject H_0. We conclude that the session has a positive effect on managerial ratings for concern for people.

CHAPTER 8

Exercises 8.1

1. H_0: The distribution is binomial with p = 0.50

   H_1: The distribution is not binomial with p = 0.50

(1) Number of Stocks Declining	(2) Number of Portfolios f_o	(3) (Col. 1 × Col. 2)	(4) $f(x)$	(5) Expected Number of Failures (Col. 4 × 2,000) f_t
0	50	0	0.031	62
1	405	405	0.156	312
2	485	907	0.313	626
3	585	1,755	0.313	626
4	475	1,900	0.156	312
5	0	0	0.031	62
Total	2,000	5,030	1.000	2,000

$$\bar{p} = \frac{5{,}030}{2{,}000 \times 5} = 0.503$$

$\chi^2 = 211.65$

$\nu = 5$

$\chi^2_{0.01} = 13.277$

Reject H_0 and conclude that the binomial distribution with p = 0.50 is not a good fit.

2. H_0: The distribution is Poisson with μ = 2.6

   H_1: The distribution is not Poisson with μ = 2.6

(1) Number of Plants	(2) Number of Countries Observed f_o	(3) Column 1 × Column 2	(4) $f(x)$	(5) Expected Number of Countries f_t
0	6	0	0.074	7.4
1	7	7	0.193	19.3
2	40	80	0.251	25.1
3	24	72	0.218	21.8
4	14	56	0.141	14.1
5 or more	9	45	0.123	12.3
Total	100	260	1.000	100.0

Mean = 260/100 = 2.6

χ^2 = 18.195

ν = 4

$\chi^2_{0.01}$ = 13.277

Hence, reject H_0 and conclude that the Poisson distribution with μ = 2.6 is not a good fit.

3. H_0: The four major currencies performed equally well against the cruzeiro

   H_1: The four major currencies did not perform equally well against the cruzeiro

(1) Currency	(2) Number of Times Cruzeiro Declined in Value f_o	(3) Expected Number of Times Cruzeiro Declined in Value f_t
German mark	10	8
Swiss franc	10	8
Japanese yen	7	8
U.S. dollar	5	8
Total	32	32

χ^2 = 2.25

ν = 3

$\chi^2_{0.05}$ = 7.815

$\chi^2_{0.01}$ = 11.345

Retain H_0 and conclude that the evidence is consistent with the hypothesis that the four major currencies performed equally well against the cruzeiro.

4. H_0: The distribution is Poisson with μ = 1.5

   H_1: The distribution is not Poisson with μ = 1.5

(1) Ratings	(2) Number of Companies f_o		(3) (Col. 1 × Col. 2)	(4) $f(x)$	(5) Expected Number of Companies f_t	
0	10		0	0.223	11.15	
1	18		18	0.335	16.75	
2	13		26	0.251	12.55	
3	6	} 9	18	0.125	6.25	} 9.35
4	2		8	0.047	2.35	
5	1		5	0.015	0.75	
Total	50		75	0.996	49.80	

Mean = 75/50 = 1.5

$\chi^2 = 0.249$

$\nu = 2$

$\chi^2_{0.05} = 5.991$

Retain H_0 and conclude that the evidence is consistent with the hypothesis that the distribution of ratings is Poisson with $\mu = 1.5$.

5. H_0: The distribution is Poisson with $\mu = 0.60$

   H_1: The distribution is not Poisson with $\mu = 0.60$

(1) Number of Errors per Page	(2) Observed Number of Pages f_o	(3) (Col. 1 × Col. 2)	(4) $f(x)$	(5) Expected Number of Pages f_t
0	1,102	0	0.549	1,098
1	657	657	0.329	658
2	193	386	0.099	198
3	35	105	0.020	40
4	13	52	0.003	6
Total	2,000	1,200	1.000	2,000

Mean = 1,200/2,000 = 0.6

$\chi^2 = 8.935$

$\nu = 3$

$\chi^2_{0.01} = 11.345$

Retain H_0 and conclude that the Poisson distribution with $\mu = 0.60$ is a good fit.

6. H_0: The department store's credit customers are drawn from a population that has an equal distribution among the six classes

   H_1: The department store's credit customers are not drawn from a population that has an equal distribution among the six classes

Classification	f_o	f_t
A	46	50
B	42	50
C	56	50
D	64	50
E	48	50
F	44	50
Total	300	300

$\chi^2 = 7.04$

$\nu = 5$

$\chi^2_{0.05} = 11.070$

Retain H_0 at $\alpha = 0.05$. We cannot reject the null hypothesis.

7. H_0: The distribution is Poisson with $\mu = 2.4$

H_1: The distribution is not Poisson with $\mu = 2.4$

(1) Number of Deaths	(2) Observed Number of Hospital-Years f_o		(3) Column 1 × Column 2	(4) $f(x)$	(5) Expected Number of Hospital-Years f_t	
0	12		0	0.091	9.1	
1	22		22	0.217	21.7	
2	30		60	0.262	26.2	
3	15		45	0.209	20.9	
4	7		28	0.125	12.5	
5	6	14	30	0.060	6.0	9.6
6	4		24	0.024	2.4	
7	2		14	0.009	0.9	
8	1		8	0.002	0.2	
9	1		9	0.001	0.1	
Total	100		240	1.000	100.0	

Mean = 240/100 = 2.4 deaths

$\chi^2 = 7.582$

$\nu = 4$

$\chi^2_{0.05} = 9.488$

$\chi^2_{0.01} = 13.277$

Hence, retain H_0 at both $\alpha = 0.05$ and $\alpha = 0.01$ and conclude that the Poisson distribution with $\mu = 2.4$ is a "good fit."

8. H_0: The bank's employees with MBA degrees are equally distributed among the four schools

H_1: The bank's employees with MBA degrees are not equally distributed among the four schools

School	f_o	f_t
A	4	6
B	9	6
C	8	6
D	3	6
Total	24	24

$\chi^2 = 4.333$

$\nu = 3$

$\chi^2_{0.05} = 7.815$

Hence, retain H_0 at $\alpha = 0.05$. We cannot reject the null hypothesis.

Exercises 8.2

1. H_0: Preferences for different magazines are independent of geographic location

   H_1: Preferences for different magazines are not independent of geographic location

f_o	f_t
75	100.0
50	81.7
175	118.3
120	100.0
85	81.7
95	118.3
105	100.0
110	81.7
85	118.3
900	900.0

   $\chi^2 = 73.875$

   $\nu = 4$

   $\chi^2_{0.05} = 9.488$

   Reject H_0 at $\alpha = 0.05$ and conclude that preferences for different magazines are not independent of geographic location.

2. H_0: Preferences for ice creams are independent of buyer's sex

   H_1: Preferences for ice creams are not independent of buyer's sex

   a. $\chi^2 = 7.50$

      $\nu = (2-1)(3-1) = 2$

      $\chi^2_{0.05} = 5.991$

      Hence, reject H_0 at $\alpha = 0.05$.

   b. $\chi^2 = 10.50$

      $\nu = (2-1)(4-1) = 3$

      $\chi^2_{0.01} = 11.345$

      Hence, retain H_0 at $\alpha = 0.01$.

3. H_0: Cash flows are independent of the company's operating leverage

   H_1: Cash flows are not independent of the company's operating leverage

f_o	f_t
6	6.0
12	12.0
2	2.0
14	13.8
28	27.6
4	4.6
10	10.2
20	20.4
4	3.4
100	100.0

$\chi^2 = 0.205$
$\nu = (3-1)(3-1) = 4$
$\chi^2_{0.01} = 13.277$

Retain H_0 and conclude that the observed data are consistent with the null hypothesis that the cash flows are independent of the company's operating leverage.

4. H_0: Impact of advertisement is independent of nature of advertisement

H_1: Impact of advertisement is not independent of nature of advertisement

f_o	f_t
75	49.5
25	50.5
23	48.5
75	49.5
198	198.0

$\chi^2 = 52.555$
$\nu = (2-1)(2-1) = 1$
$\chi^2_{0.01} = 6.635$

Reject H_0 at $\alpha = 0.01$ and conclude that impact of advertisement is not independent of nature of advertisement.

5. H_0: The proportions of stocks suffering losses does not differ among the mutual funds

H_1: The proportions of stocks suffering losses differs among the mutual funds

$$\chi^2 = \frac{(6-8.75)^2}{8.75} + \frac{(194-191.25)^2}{191.25} + \frac{(8-8.75)^2}{8.75} + \frac{(192-191.25)^2}{191.25} + \frac{(9-8.75)^2}{8.75} + \frac{(191-191.25)^2}{191.25} + \frac{(12-8.75)^2}{8.75} + \frac{(188-191.25)^2}{191.25}$$
$$= 2.240$$
$\nu = 3$
$\chi^2_{0.05} = 7.815$

Retain H_0 at $\alpha = 0.05$. We cannot conclude that the proportions of stocks suffering losses differs among these mutual funds.

6. H_0: Share prices are independent of declared dividends.

   H_1: Share prices are not independent of declared dividends.

f_o	f_t
6	6.0
12	12.0
2	2.0
14	13.8
28	27.6
4	4.6
10	10.2
20	20.4
4	3.4
100	100.0

   $\chi^2 = 0.205$
   df = (3 - 1) (3 - 1) = 4
   $\chi^2_{0.01} = 13.277$

   Since 0.205 < 13.277, we retain H_0 and conclude that share price is independent of declared dividends.

7. H_0: Proportions of stocks suffering losses do not differ among affiliates.

   H_1: Proportions of stocks suffering losses do differ among affiliates.

$$\chi^2 = \frac{(6-8.75)^2}{8.75} + \frac{(194-191.25)^2}{191.25} + \frac{(8-8.75)^2}{8.75}$$
$$+ \frac{(192-191.25)^2}{191.25} + \frac{(9-8.75)^2}{8.75} + \frac{(191-191.25)^2}{191.25}$$
$$+ \frac{(12-8.75)^2}{8.75} + \frac{(188-191.25)^2}{191.25}$$
$$= 2.241$$

   df = (4 - 1) (2 - 1) = 3
   $\chi^2_{0.05} = 7.815$

   Since 2.24 < 7.815, retain H_0 at $\alpha = 0.05$ and conclude that the proportions of stocks suffering losses do not differ among affiliates.

Exercises 8.3

1. H_0: Type of water does not influence the effectiveness of the detergent

   H_1: Type of water influences the effectiveness of the detergent

Analysis of variance table

Source of Variation	Sum of Squares	Degrees of Freedom	Mean Square
Between water types	82.67	2	41.335
Within water types	42.00	9	4.667
Total	124.67	11	

   $F(2, 9) = 41{,}335/4.667 = 8.86$
   $F_{0.01}(2, 9) = 8.02$

   Since 8.86 > 8.02, reject H_0 and conclude that the type of water used influences the effectiveness of the detergent.

2. H_0: The collectors are equally successful in collecting overdue accounts

   H_1: The collectors are not equally successful in collecting overdue accounts

Analysis of variance table

Source of Variation	Sum of Squares	Degrees of Freedom	Mean Square
Between collectors	430	2	215
Within collectors	580	12	48.33
Total	1,010	14	

$F(2, 12) = 215/48.33 = 4.45$
$F_{0.05}(2, 12) = 3.88$

Since 4.45 > 3.88, reject H_0 and conclude that the collectors are not equally successful in collecting overdue accounts.

3. H_0: No difference exists among the profit levels of the three classes of firms

   H_1: A difference exists among the profit levels of the three classes of firms

Analysis of variance table

Source of Variation	Sum of Squares	Degrees of Freedom	Mean Square
Between classes of firms	264.73	2	132.365
Within classes of firms	175.67	7	25.096
Total	440.40	9	

$F(2, 7) = 132.365/25.096 = 5.27$
$F_{0.01}(2, 7) = 9.55$

Since 5.27 < 9.55, retain H_0. The data are consistent with the hypothesis of no difference among profit levels of the three classes of firms.

4. H_0: The average ratios of expected return to standard deviation do not differ among the three industries

   H_1: The average ratios of expected return to standard deviation differ among the three industries

Analysis of variance table

Source of Variation	Sum of Squares	Degrees of Freedom	Mean Square
Between industries	0.507	2	0.254
Within industries	0.222	6	0.037
Total	0.729	8	

$F(2, 6) = 0.254/0.037 = 6.86$
$F_{0.05}(2, 6) = 5.14$

Since 6.86 > 5.14, reject H_0. Conclude that the average ratios of expected return to standard deviation differ among the three industries.

5. Two-factor analysis of variance table (sales figures in millions of dollars)

Source of Variation	Sum of Squares	Degrees of Freedom	Mean Square
Sales discount rates	2.896	2	1.448
Advertising expenditure	0.176	2	0.088
Error	0.057	4	0.0143
Total	3.129	8	

(1) H_0: No difference in sales exists at the three levels of advertising

H_1: A difference in sales at the three levels of advertising

$F(2, 4) = 1.448/0.0143 = 101.26$
$F_{0.01}(2, 4) = 18.00$

Since 101.26 > 18.00, reject H_0 and conclude that sales differ with respect to the three levels of advertising.

(2) H_0: No difference in sales exists for three rates of sales discounts

H_1: A difference in sales exists for three rates of sales discounts

$F(2, 4) = 0.088/0.0143 = 6.154$
$F_{0.01}(2, 4) = 18.00$

Since 6.154 < 18.00, retain H_0. We cannot conclude that sales differ with respect to the three sales discount rates.

6. Two-factor analysis of variance table

Source of Variation	Sum of Squares	Degrees of Freedom	Mean Square
Relative prices	20.016	3	6.672
National income	0.487	2	0.244
Error	6.446	6	1.074
Total	26.949	11	

(1) H_0: There is no difference in national trade surpluses (deficits) among the three levels of national income

H_1: There is a difference in the national trade surpluses (deficits) among the three levels of national income

$F(2, 6) = 0.244/1.074 = 0.227$
$F_{0.05}(2, 6) = 5.14$

Since 0.227 < 5.14, retain H_0 and conclude that national trade surpluses (deficits) do not differ among the three levels of national income.

(2) H_0: There is no difference in national trade surpluses (deficits) at the four levels of relative prices

H_1: There is a difference in national trade surpluses (deficits) at the four levels of relative prices

$F(3, 6) = 6.672/1.074 = 6.21$
$F_{0.05}(3, 6) = 4.76$

Since 6.21 > 4.76, reject H_0 and conclude that national trade surpluses (deficits) differ at the four levels of relative prices.

7. H_0: There is no difference in performance among the three pension funds

H_1: There is a difference in performance among the three pension funds

Analysis of variance table

Source of Variation	Sum of Squares	Degrees of Freedom	Mean Square	F
Between pension funds	21,332.87	2	10,666.44	250.27
Within pension funds	1,150.87	27	42.62	
Total	22,483.74	29		

$F(2, 27) = 250.27$
$F_{0.05}(2, 27) = 3.35$

Since 250.27 > 3.35, reject H_0 and conclude that real differences in performance exist among the three pension funds.

8. Two-factor analysis of variance table

Source of Variation	Sum of Squares	Degrees of Freedom	Mean Square	F
Operators	11.19	3	3.73	2.66
Machines	5.69	3	1.90	1.36
Error	12.56	9	1.40	
Total	29.44	15		

H_0: The operators do not differ with respect to average output per minute

H_1: The operators differ with respect to average output per minute

$F(3, 9) = 3.73/1.40 = 2.66$
$F_{0.01}(3, 9) = 6.99$

Since 2.66 < 6.99, accept H_0.

H_0: The machines do not differ with respect to average output per minute

H_1: The machines differ with respect to average output per minute

$F(3, 9) = 1.9/1.4 = 1.36$
$F_{0.01}(3, 9) = 6.99$

Since 1.36 < 6.99, retain H_0.

9. Analysis of variance table

Source of Variation	Sum of Squares	Degrees of Freedom	Mean Square	F
Countries	26	2	13	13/0.5 = 26
Years	122	2	61	61/0.5 = 122
Error	2	4	0.5	
Total	150	8		

a. H_0: The debt-to-asset ratio is the same for all countries.

H_1: The debt-to-asset ratio is not the same for all countries.

$F_{0.05}(2, 4) = 6.94$

Since 26 > 6.94, reject H_0.

b. H_0: The debt-to-asset ratio is the same for the selected years.

H_1: The debt-to-asset ratio is not the same for the selected years.

$F_{0.05}(2, 4) = 6.94$

Since 122 > 6.94, reject H_0.

10. H_0: No difference in performance exists among the three funds.

H_1: Performances differ among the three funds.

Analysis of variance table

Source of Variation	Sum of Squares	Degrees of Freedom	Mean Square
Between funds	21,332.87	2	10,666.44
Within each fund	2,667.0	27	98.78
Total	22,483.74	29	--

$F(2, 27) = 107.98$
$F_{0.05}(2, 27) = 3.35$

Since 107.98 > 3.35, reject H_0, and conclude that there are real differences in performance among the three funds.

11. H_0: There are no differences in average ratings among the officers.

H_1: There are differences in average ratings among the officers.

Analysis of variance table

Source of Variation	Sum of Squares	Degrees of Freedom	Mean Square
Between officers	22	2	11
Within each officer	120	30	4
Total	142	32	--

$F(2, 30) = 2.75$
$F_{0.05}(2, 30) = 3.32$

Since 2.75 < 3.32, we retain H_0 at $\alpha = 0.05$ and conclude that the personnel officers do not differ in their average ratings.

REVIEW EXERCISES FOR CHAPTERS 6 THROUGH 8

1. a. H_0: $p \le 0.50$ $\quad\quad \bar{p} = \frac{33}{60} = 0.55$

H_1: $p > 0.50$

$\alpha = 0.05$

$$\text{Critical value} = 0.50 + (1.65)\sqrt{\frac{(0.50)(0.50)}{60}} = 0.6065$$

Since 0.55 < 0.6065, we retain H_0. We conclude that the data do not support the claim that more than 50% of the students are made sensitive to ethical issues if given the module.

b. $P(\text{Type II error}) = P(\text{Retain } H_0 | p = .60)$

$$= P\left(z \le \frac{0.6065 - 0.60}{\sqrt{(0.6)(0.4)/60}}\right) = P(z \le 0.1028)$$

$$= .5 + 0.398 = 0.5398$$

We could decrease the probability of Type II errors and thus improve the performance of the test by increasing the sample size.

c. H_0: $p_1 - p_2 \le 0$

H_1: $p_1 - p_2 > 0$

$\alpha = 0.02$

$$\hat{p} = \frac{60(0.55) + 60(.45)}{60 + 60} = 0.50$$

$$s_{\bar{p}_1 - \bar{p}_2} = \sqrt{(0.50)(0.50)\left(\frac{1}{60} + \frac{1}{60}\right)} = 0.0913$$

Critical value = 0 + (2.05)(0.0913) = 0.1872

Since $\bar{p}_1 - \bar{p}_2 = .55 - .45 = .10 < 0.1872$, we retain H_0. We conclude that the students who were given the module are not more sensitive to ethical issues than those who were not given the module.

2. a. H_0: $p \le 0.5$ $\quad\quad \bar{p} = \frac{60}{100} = 0.60$

H_1: $p > 0.5$

$\alpha = 0.01$

$$\text{Critical value} = 0.50 + 2.33\sqrt{\frac{(0.5)(0.5)}{100}} = 0.6165$$

Since 0.60 < 0.6165, we retain H_0. The union cannot be fairly certain that the proportion of favorable union members exceeds 0.5.

b. $P(\text{Type II error}) = P(\text{Retain } H_0|p = 0.64)$

$$P(\bar{p} \le .6165|p = 0.64) = P\left(z \le \frac{0.6165 - .64}{\sqrt{(0.64)(0.36)/100}}\right)$$

$$P(z \le 0.49) = 0.3121$$

3. H_0: $\mu_1 = \mu_2$

H_1: $\mu_1 \ne \mu_2$

$$s_{\bar{x}_1 - \bar{x}_2} = \sqrt{\frac{(\$650)^2}{60} + \frac{(\$700)^2}{34}} = \$146.47$$

$$z_0 = \frac{\$15{,}500 - \$14{,}600}{\$146.47} = 6.14$$

$$P(|z| > 6.14) = 0.00$$

Therefore, it is highly unlikely that the difference in mean starting salaries is simply due to chance.

Assumptions: The samples of men and women are random samples of all men and women employed by the company during the year for this entry-level position. In the statistical test, the applicability of the central limit theorem was assumed.

4. a. H_0: $p \ge 0.20$

H_1: $p < 0.20$

Critical value = 68/400 = 0.17

$$\text{Critical } z = \frac{0.17 - 0.20}{\sqrt{\frac{(0.20)(0.80)}{400}}} = -1.50$$

$$\alpha = 0.5000 - 0.4332 = .0668$$

Nature of the Type I error: incorrectly discontinuing marketing of the product, that is discontinuing marketing when $p \ge 0.20$.

b. $$z = \frac{0.17 - 0.15}{\sqrt{\frac{(0.15)(0.85)}{400}}} = 1.12$$

$$\beta = P(z > 1.12) = 0.5000 - 0.3686 = 0.1314$$

5. a. $$z = \frac{600 - 500}{80} = 1.25$$

$$P(X > 600) = P(z > 1.25) = 0.5000 - 0.3944 = 0.1056$$

b.

f_o	f_t	$(f_o - f_t)^2/f_t$
20	10.56	8.44
60	78.88	4.52
20	10.56	8.44
100	100.00	$\chi^2 = 21.40$

$\chi^2_{0.05,2} = 5.991$

Since 21.40 > 5.991, we conclude that the test results do not support ETA's statement that GMAT scores are normally distributed with $\mu = 500$ and $\sigma = 80$.

6\. a. H_0: $\mu \le 5$ $\alpha = 0.05$
H_1: $\mu > 5$ $\nu = 5 - 1 = 4$

Critical value $= 5 + 2.132\left(\frac{0.6}{\sqrt{5}}\right) = 5.572$

Since $\bar{x} = 6 > 5.572$, reject H_0. This implies that it is safe to hire high school graduates.

b. H_0: $\mu_3 - \mu_1 = 0$ $\alpha = 0.05$
H_1: $\mu_3 - \mu_1 \ne 0$ $\nu = (5 - 1) + (5 - 1) = 8$

$$\hat{s}^2 = \frac{4(0.25) + 4(0.36)}{4 + 4} = 0.305$$

$$t = \frac{\bar{x}_3 - \bar{x}_1}{s_{\bar{x}_3 - x_1}} = \frac{8 - 6}{(\sqrt{0.305})\left(\sqrt{\frac{1}{5} + \frac{1}{5}}\right)} = 5.73$$

$t_{0.05,8} = 2.306$

Since 5.73 > 2.306, reject H_0, and conclude that there is a difference in performance of high school graduates and MBAs.

c.

Source of Variation	Sum of Squares	Degrees of Freedom	Mean Square
Between Groups	10	2	5
Within Groups	5	12	5/12
Total	15	14	

Note:

$s_1^2 = \Sigma(X_1 - \bar{X}_1)^2/(n_1 - 1)$
$\Sigma(X_1 - \bar{X}_1)^2 = (n_1 - 1)s_1^2$

$SSA = 5(6 - 7)^2 + 5(7 - 7)^2 + 5(8 - 7)^2 = 10$
$SSE = 4(0.36) + 4(0.64) + 4(0.25) = 5$

$$F(2, 12) = \frac{5}{5/12} = 12$$
$F_{0.05}(2, 12) = 3.88$

Since 12 > 3.88, reject H_0. Conclude that there are differences in performance among the three groups.

7\. a. $P(\bar{x} \ge 41.32) = P\left(z \ge \frac{41.32 - 30}{30.84/\sqrt{22}}\right) = P(z \ge 1.72) = 0.0427$

Assumptions: Purchase of clothing is identically distributed (from one person to another) and is normally distributed. The key assumption is normality. $\bar{X}$ will approach normality by the central limit theorem as sample size increases, but it is apparent from the data that the population distribution is not normal. In fact, there probably are a number of zero purchases and extreme observations in the population.

b. $\$41.32 \pm (2.08)(\$30.84)/\sqrt{22} = \$27.64$ to $\$55.00$

c. H_0: $\mu \le \$30$

H_1: $\mu > \$30$

Critical value = $\$30 + (2.518)(\$30.84/\sqrt{22}) = \$46.56$

Since $\bar{x} = 41.32 < \$46.56$, we retain H_0. The data do not support the belief that the average has increased.

8. a. $\bar{p} = \dfrac{150}{250} = 0.6$

Confidence interval

$$0.6 \pm 1.645\sqrt{\frac{(0.6)(0.4)}{250}} = 0.549 \text{ to } 0.651$$

b. $n \ge (2.33)^2(1/4)/(0.01)^2 = 13{,}572.25$

Cost = 13,573($2.50) = $33,931

9. a. H_0: $\mu = 0.075$

H_1: $\mu > 0.075$

$\alpha = 0.05$

Critical value = $0.075 + 1.65(0.002) = 0.0783$

Since $0.078 < 0.0783$, retain H_0. We cannot conclude that there has been a change in the average interest rate.

b. $z = \dfrac{0.0783 - 0.0775}{0.02/\sqrt{100}} = 0.4$

Power = $P(\bar{x} > 0.0783) = P(z > 0.4) = 0.5000 - 0.1554 = 0.3446$

10. a. H_0: $p \le 0.50$

H_1: $p > 0.50$

$\alpha = 0.05$

Critical value = $.50 + 1.65\sqrt{\dfrac{(0.50)(0.50)}{30}} = 0.65$

Since $0.67 > 0.65$, reject H_0. Conclude that the data support the claim.

b. $\dfrac{0.65 - 0.60}{\sqrt{\dfrac{(.6)(.4)}{30}}} = 0.56$

$P(\text{Retain } H_0 | p = 0.60) = P(\bar{p} < 0.65 | p = 0.60) = P(z < 0.56) = 0.7123$

11. a. H_0: $\mu \le 50$

H_1: $\mu > 50$

$\alpha = 0.05$

Critical value = $50 + 1.711\dfrac{\sqrt{466}}{\sqrt{55}} = 57.39$

Since $\bar{x}_1 = 62 > 57$, the claim that the mean rating for the first advertisement exceeds 50 is supported by the data.

b. H_0: $\mu_3 = \mu_4$
H_1: $\mu_3 \neq \mu_4$
$\alpha = 0.05$

Critical values = $0 \pm 2.01\sqrt{465}\sqrt{\frac{1}{25} + \frac{1}{25}} = \pm 12.26$

Since $\bar{x}_3 - \bar{x}_4 = -14$, reject H_0. The data support the claim that the mean ratings of the third and fourth advertisements are different.

c.

Source of Variation	Sum of Squares	Degrees of Freedom	Mean Square
Between Advertisements	3,000	3	1,000
Within Advertisements	43,589	96	454
Total	46,584	99	

$SSA = 25[62-60)^2 + (56-60)^2 + (54-60)^2 + (68-60)^2] = 3{,}000$
$SSE = 24[466 + 420 + 422 + 508] = 43{,}584$

$F(3, 96) = \frac{1{,}000}{454} = 2.2026$
$F_{0.05}\ (3, 96) = 2.70$

Since $2.2026 < 2.70$, we retain the possibility that $\mu_1 = \mu_2 = \mu_3 = \mu_4$. Hence, the data do not support the claim that the means of the four advertisements are not the same.

12. a.

Source of Variation	Sum of Squares	Degrees of Freedom	Mean Square
Between industries	1,340	2	670
Within industries	2,530	27	93.70
Total	3,870	29	

$SSA = 10[(21-14)^2 + (16-14)^2 + (5-14)^2] = 1{,}340$
$SSE = 9[(87.78) + (98.89) + (94.44)] = 2{,}530$

$F(2, 27) = 670/93.7 = 7.15$
$F_{0.05}\ (2, 27) = 3.35$

Since $7.15 > 3.35$, conclude that the mean yields of the three industries differ.

b. See figure.

Observed

	A	B	
I	2	8	10
II	5	5	10
III	8	2	10
	15	15	30

Expected

	A	B	
I	5	5	10
II	5	5	10
III	5	5	10
	15	15	30

Figure for exercise 12(b)

$$\chi^2 = \frac{(2-5)^2}{5} + \frac{(8-5)^2}{5} + \frac{(5-5)^2}{5} + \frac{(5-5)^2}{5} + \frac{(8-5)^2}{5} + \frac{(2-5)^2}{5} = 7.2$$

$\chi^2_{0.05,2} = 5.99$

Since 7.2 > 5.99, conclude that there is dependence between industry classification and percentage yield.

13. a. $\sigma_{\bar{x}} = 0.5/\sqrt{144} = 0.0417$

$\bar{x} \pm 1.96\ \sigma_{\bar{x}} = 3.15 \pm 1.96(0.0417) = 3.0683$ to 3.2317 mg

b. $n = (1.96)^2\ (0.5)^2/(0.06)^2 = 267$

14. a. H_0: $\mu_1 - \mu_2 = 0$

H_1: $\mu_1 - \mu_2 \neq 0$

$\alpha = 0.01$

$s_{\bar{x}_1 - \bar{x}_2} = \sqrt{5^2/100 + 12^2/100} = 1.3$

Critical $\bar{x}_1 - \bar{x}_2 = 0 \pm 2.58(1.3) = \pm 3.354$

Since $19.0 - 24.5 = -5.5 < -3.354$, reject H_0 and conclude that there is a difference in average coffee consumption in the two regions.

b. True, because of symmetry in the power curve.

c. False. The size of the critical region decreases.

d. False. $\alpha + \beta \neq 1$. However, for a fixed sample size, increasing α does bring about decreases in probabilities of Type II errors.

15. a. $\bar{p} = 70/200 = 0.35$

b. $\bar{p} = 0.35$ is an estimate of $\mu_{\bar{p}}$,

$s^2_{\bar{p}} = (0.35)(0.65)/200 = 0.00228$ is an estimate of $\sigma^2_{\bar{p}}$.

c. $\bar{p} \pm 2.33\ s_{\bar{p}} = 0.35 \pm (2.33)(0.048) = 0.35 \pm 0.11 = 0.24$ to 0.46

16. a. $10 \pm 2.17(4.5/\sqrt{64}) = 8.78$ to 11.22 minutes

b. $n = (2.57)^2(6)^2/3^2 = 26.4 \approx 27$

c. $10 + z\sqrt{20.25}/\sqrt{64} = 10.721$ $\quad z = 1.282$ $\quad$ 80% confidence interval

17. a. $\chi^2 = (15-20)^2/20 + (50-30)^2/30 + (5-20)^2/20 = 25.83$

$\chi^2_{0.05,2} = 5.991$

Since 25.83 > 5.991, reject H_0. The data do not support the hypothesis that the incomes are in the ratio 2:3:2.

b. H_0: The three areas are alike in their income profiles. That is, incomes and area are independent.

H_1: The three areas are not alike in their income profiles.

$\chi^2 = (15-23.9)^2/23.9 + (50-25.6)^2/25.6 + \cdots + (50-25.6)^2/25.6 = 23.3$

Since 23.3 > 13.277, reject H_0 and conclude that the three areas are not alike in their income profiles.

18. a. H_0: $\mu = 200$
H_1: $\mu < 200$
$\alpha = 0.05$
$\sigma_{\bar{x}} = \$42/\sqrt{9} = \$14$

Critical $\bar{x} = \$200 - (1.65)(\$14) = \$176.90$

Decision Rule

1. If $\bar{x} < 176.90$, reject H_0
2. If $\bar{x} \geq 176.90$, retain H_0

Conclusion: Since \$188 > 176.90, retain H_0. Therefore, we cannot reject the hypothesis that the population of additional stores has a monthly sales mean of \$200.

b. H_0: $\mu = \$200$
H_1: $\mu < \$200$
$\alpha = 0.05$

Critical t value for $\nu = 9 - 1 = 8$, one tailed test = -1.86.

Decision Rule

1. If $t < -1.86$, reject H_0
2. If $t \geq -1.86$, retain H_0

$$t = \frac{\$188 - \$200}{\$\sqrt{350}/\sqrt{9}} = -1.92$$

Conclusion: Since -1.92 < -1.86, reject H_0. Therefore, we reject the hypothesis that the population of additional stores has a monthly sales mean of \$200.

c. $z_0 = (176.90 - \$162.90)/\$14 = 1$
$\beta = P(z > 1) = 0.5000 - 0.3413 = 0.16$

19. a. $12 \pm (1.96)\,5/\sqrt{25} = 10.4\%$ to 13.96%

b. $n = (1.96)^2(0.5)^2/(0.05)^2 = 384.16 = 385$

c. $P[z_0 < (X_0 - 0.12)/0.05] = 0.10$
$-1.28 = (x_0 - 0.12)/0.05$
$x_0 = 0.056 = 5.6\%$

20. a. H_0: $p_1 = 0.60$, $p_2 = 20$, $p_3 = 0.20$
H_1: No so

$\chi^2 = (110 - 120)^2/120 + (40 - 40)^2/40 + (50 - 40)^2/40 = 3.33$

$\chi^2_{0.01,2} = 9.21$

Since 3.33 < 9.21, retain H_0 and conclude that the percentages observed in the sample of 200 offers are not inconsistent with the claimed percentages.

b. H_0: Acceptances and rejections of offers are independent of type of option.

H_1: Acceptances and rejections of offers are not independent of type of option.

$$\chi^2 = \frac{(61-66)^2}{66} + \frac{(49-44)^2}{44} + \frac{(25-24)^2}{24} + \frac{(15-16)^2}{16} + \frac{(34-30)^2}{30} + \frac{(16-20)^2}{20}$$

$= 2.38$

$\nu = (2-1)(3-1) = 2$

$\chi^2_{0.05,2} = 5.99$

Since 2.38 < 5.99, retain H_0. We cannot conclude that the type of option affects the acceptance or rejection of offers.

21. a. H_0: $p \le 0.25$

H_1: $p > 0.25$

Critical $\bar{p} = 0.25 + 1.65\sqrt{(0.25)(0.75)/100} = 0.321$

Decision Rule

1. If $\bar{p} > 0.321$, reject H_0
2. If $\bar{p} \le 0.321$, retain H_0

Conclusion: Since 0.35 > 0.321, reject H_0. Yes, there is a statistically significant result indicating that the company should proceed with the manufacturing of the prototype.

b. H_0: $\mu \le 105$

H_1: $\mu > 105$

$\alpha = 0.01$

Critical $\bar{x} = 105 + (2.33)21/\sqrt{36} = 113.155$

Since 111 < 113.155, retain H_0. Manufacturing should not begin.

c. $P(\text{Retain } H_0 | \mu = 110) = P(\bar{x} \le 113.155 | \mu = 110)$

$= P\left(z \le \frac{113.155 - 110}{21/\sqrt{36}}\right) = P(z \le 0.901) = 0.8159$

22. a. H_0: $\mu_{ML} = \mu_{NP}$

H_1: $\mu_{ML} \ne \mu_{NP}$

$\alpha = 0.01$

$\hat{s}^2 = [6(0.081) + 10(0.072)]/(6 + 10) = 0.075375$

$s_{\bar{x}_{ML} - \bar{x}_{NP}} = \sqrt{0.075375}\sqrt{1/7 + 1/11} = 0.1327$

$t = (3.7 - 3.4)/0.1327 = 2.26$

$t_{0.01,16} = 2.921$

Since 2.26 < 2.921, retain H_0. Therefore, the result supports the claim of virtually identical weight.

b. H_0: $\mu_{NP} \ge \mu_{ML}$

$\mu_{NP} < \mu_{ML}$

$t = 2.26$

$t_{0.05,16}$ in a one-tailed test = 1.746

Since 2.26 > 1.746, reject H_0

c. $3.7 + t\sqrt{0.081}/\sqrt{7} = 4.038$

$t = 3.143$

Since $\nu = 6$, we find this t value to pertain to a 98% confidence level.

23\. a. $z = \dfrac{18.75 - 18}{1.8/\sqrt{36}} = 2.5$

P(Type I error) = 1 - 2(0.4938) = 0.0124

A Type I error in this situation is the erroneous rejection of the null hypothesis that the process is producing at a level of μ = 18 pounds.

b. See figure.

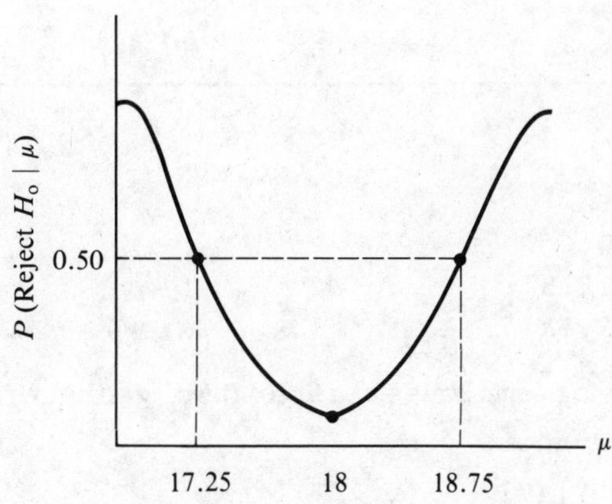

Figure for exercise 23(b)

c. (i) False
(ii) False
(iii) False
(iv) True
(v) True

CHAPTER 9

Exercises 9.4

1. a = Y intercept = 20
   b = slope = 50/4 = 12.5
   $\hat{Y} = a + bX = 20 + 12.5X$

2. a. Y = Merit rating of employees after two years of service

   X = Aptitude test score

   $$b = \frac{5{,}759 - 10(80.7)(7)}{66{,}707 - 10(80.7)^2} = 0.0695$$

   $a = 7 - 0.0695(80.7) = 1.3914$

   $\hat{Y} = 1.3914 + 0.0695X$

   $\hat{Y}$: 6,604, 5.839, 7.785, 6.951, 6.673, 5.422, 8.063, 7.577, 8.202, 6.882

   b. The regression coefficient $b = 0.0695$ means that for two employees whose aptitude scores differ by one point, the estimated difference in their merit ratings is 0.0695 points.

   c. $\hat{Y} = 1.3914 + (0.0695)(90) = 7.646$

3. (1) The first purpose of regression analysis is to provide estimates of values of the dependent variable from values of the independent variable. The regression line and its equation (the regression equation) are used for this purpose.
   (2) The second objective of regression analysis is to obtain measures of the error involved in using the regression line for estimation. The standard error of estimate and related measures are useful for this purpose.
   (3) The third objective (correlation analysis) is to obtain a measure of the degree of association between the two variables. The coefficient of determination measures the strength of the relationship between the variables.

4. a. $$b = \frac{4{,}470 - (45)(14.16)(5.2)}{10{,}124 - (45)(14.16)^2} = 1.05$$

   $a = 5.2 - (1.05)(14.16) = -9.668$

   $\hat{Y} = -9.668 + 1.05X$

   b. $\hat{Y} = -9.668 + 1.05(12) = 2.932$ or 3 defective articles

5. a. Y = interest rate (percent)

   X = issue size (millions of dollars)

   $$b = \frac{2907.5 - (14)(25)(7.5)}{11{,}950 - (14)(25)^2} = 0.0883$$

$a = 7.5 - (0.0883)(25) = 5.2925$

$\hat{Y} = 5.2925 + 0.0883X$

b. $\hat{Y} = 5.2925 + 0.0883(35) = 8.38\%$

c. (1) A linear relationship exists between $\mu_{Y.X}$ and X.
(2) The Y values are independent of one another.
(3) The conditional probability distributions of Y given X are normal.
(4) The conditional standard deviations, $\sigma_{Y.X}$, are equal for all values of X.

6. a. $\hat{Y}$ = return on average investment (percent)

X = market share (percent)

$$b = \frac{2,940.30 - [(5)(25.40)(18.84)]}{4,371.00 - [(5)(25.40)^2]}$$

$$= \frac{547.62}{1,145.20} = 0.48$$

$a = 18.84 - [(0.48)(25.40)] = 6.65$

$\hat{Y} = 6.65 + 0.48X$

$\hat{Y}$: 8.57%; 23.93%; 18.65%; 13.85%; 29.21%

b. A regression coefficient of $b = 0.48$ means that for two products with market-share levels that differ by 1 percentage point, the estimated difference in the return on average investment for these two products is 0.48 percentage points.

c. $\hat{Y} = 6.65 + [(0.48)(30)] = 21.05\%$

Exercise 9.5

1. a. $$b = \frac{1,364,600 - (100)(550)(21)}{38,124,400 - (100)(302,500)}$$

$$= \frac{209,600}{7,874,400} = 0.027$$

$a = 21 - (0.027)(550) = 6.15$

$\hat{Y} = 6.15 + 0.027X$

b. $$s_{Y.X} = \sqrt{\frac{50,500 - (6.15)(2,100) - (0.027)(1,364,600)}{98}}$$

$= \sqrt{7.559} = 2.75$ (thousands of dollars)

c. For a graduate with a GMAT score of 655, $6.15 + (0.027)(655) = 23.835$ (thousands of dollars).

For a graduate with a GMAT score of 500, $6.15 + (0.027)(500) = 19.650$ (thousands of dollars).

d. For a graduate with a GMAT score of 655,

$$s_{\hat{Y}} = s_{Y.X}\sqrt{\frac{1}{100} + \frac{(655 - 550)^2}{38,124,400 - (55,000)^2/100}}$$

$= (2.75)\sqrt{0.0114} = 0.2936$ (thousands of dollars)

The estimated interval is $23.835 \pm (1.98)(0.2936) = 23.835 \pm 0.5813$, or from \$23.254 to \$24.416 (thousand).

For a graduate with a GMAT score of 500,

$$s_{\hat{Y}} = s_{Y.X}\sqrt{\frac{1}{100} + \frac{(500-550)^2}{38{,}124{,}400 - (55{,}000)^2/100}}$$

$$= (2.75)\sqrt{0.0103} = 0.279$$

The estimated interval is 19.65 ± (1.98)(0.279) = 19.650 ± 0.552, or from \$19.098 to \$20.202 (thousand).

2. a. Y = earnings (in millions of dollars) in 1990

X = research and development expenditures (in millions of dollars) in 1989

$$b = \frac{10{,}186.5 - (15)(6.2)(73)}{895 - (15)(6.2)^2} = 10.671$$

$$a = 73 - (10.671)(6.2) = 6.840$$

$$Y = 6.840 + 10.671X$$

b. $\hat{Y} = 6.840 + 10.671(10) = 113.55$

c. $$s_{Y.X} = \sqrt{\frac{122{,}825 - (6.84)(1095) - (10.671)(10{,}186.5)}{13}}$$

$$= \sqrt{510.389} = 22.592 \text{ millions of dollars)}$$

The standard error of estimate measures the scatter of the observed values of Y around the corresponding computed $\hat{Y}$ values on the regression line.

d. $$s_{\hat{Y}} = s_{Y.X}\sqrt{\frac{1}{15} + \frac{(10-6.2)^2}{895 - (93)^2/15}} = (22.592)\sqrt{0.1121} = 7.564$$

The estimated interval is 113.55 ± (2.160)(7.564) = 113.55 ± 16.338, or from \$97.212 million to \$129.888 million.

3. a. Y = Income taxes paid in 1990 (millions of dollars)

X = Reported income in 1990 (millions of dollars)

$$b = \frac{324{,}950 - (12)(220)(100)}{714{,}500 - (12)(220)^2}$$

$$= \frac{60{,}950}{133{,}700} = 0.456$$

$$a = 100 - (0.456)(220) = -0.32$$

$$\hat{Y} = -0.32 + 0.456X$$

b. $$s_{Y.X} = \sqrt{\frac{148{,}300 - (-0.32)(1200) - (0.456)(324{,}950)}{10}}$$

$$= \sqrt{50.68} = 7.119$$

c. For two firms whose reported incomes differ by \$1 million, the estimated difference in the income taxes paid by the two firms is \$456,000. The weighted average income tax rate computed by dividing total income taxes paid by total reported income is 0.455; this number is very close to the regression coefficient calculated above.

d. For \$100 million reported income:

$$s_{\hat{Y}} = s_{Y.X}\sqrt{\frac{1}{12} + \frac{(100-220)^2}{714{,}500 - (2640)^2/12}}$$

$$= (7.119)\sqrt{0.191}$$

$$= \$3.111 \text{ million}$$

The estimated interval is 45.28 ± (2.228)(3.111) = 45.28 ± 6.931, or from \$38.349 million to \$52.211 million. The width of the interval is \$13.862 million.

For \$220 million reported income:

$$s_{\hat{Y}} = s_{Y.X}\sqrt{\frac{1}{12} + \frac{(220-220)^2}{714{,}500 - (2640)^2/12}}$$

$$= (7.119)\sqrt{0.0833}$$

$$= 2.055$$

The estimated interval is 100 ± (2.228)(2.055) = 100 ± 4.579, or from \$95.421 million to \$104.579 million. The width of the interval is \$9.158 million.

For \$340 million reported income:

$$s_{\hat{Y}} = s_{Y.X}\sqrt{\frac{1}{12} + \frac{(340-220)^2}{714{,}500 - (2640)^2/12}}$$

$$= (7.119)\sqrt{0.191}$$

$$= 3.111$$

The estimated interval is 154.72 ± (2.228)(3.111) = 154.72 ± 6.931, or from \$147.789 million to \$161.651 million. The width of the interval is \$13.862 million. As expected, the farther the X value is from $\bar{X}$, the wider is the interval.

e. For \$100 million reported income:

$$s_{\text{IND}} = s_{Y.X}\sqrt{1 + \frac{1}{12} + \frac{(100-220)^2}{714{,}500 - (2640)^2/12}}$$

$$= (7.119)\sqrt{1.191}$$

$$= \$7.769$$

The estimated interval is 45.28 ± (2.228)(7.769) = 45.28 ± 17.309, or from \$27.971 million to \$62.589 million. The width of the interval is \$34.618 million.

For \$220 million reported income:

$$s_{\text{IND}} = s_{Y.X}\sqrt{1 + \frac{1}{12} + \frac{(220-220)^2}{714{,}500 - (2640)^2/12}}$$

$$= (7.119)\sqrt{1.0833}$$

$$= 7.410$$

The estimated interval is 100 ± (2.228)(7.410) = 100 ± 16.509, or from \$83.491 million to \$116.509 million. The width of the interval is \$33.018 million.

For $340 million reported income:

$$s_{IND} = \sqrt{1 + \frac{1}{12} + \frac{(340-220)^2}{714{,}500 - (2640)^2/12}}$$

$$= (7.119)\sqrt{1.191}$$

$$= 7.769$$

The estimated interval is 154.72 ± (2.228)(7.769) = 154.72 ± 17.309, or from $137.419 million to $172.029 million. The width of the interval is $34.618 million. As was the case with the confidence intervals in part (d), the farther the X value is from $\overline{X}$, the wider is the prediction interval.

4. a. Y = First year sales (millions of dollars)

X = Customer awareness (percent)

$b = [39{,}815 - (14)(40)(55)]/[28{,}750 - (14)(40)^2] = 1.42$

$a = 55 - (1.42)(40) = -1.80$

$\hat{Y} = -1.80 + 1.42X$

b. $s_{Y.X} = \sqrt{[56{,}476 - (-1.8)(770) - 1.42(39.815)]/12}$

$= \sqrt{110.392} = 10.507$ (millions of dollars)

See footnote 2 of Chapter 9.

c. $$s_{\hat{Y}} = s_{Y.X}\sqrt{\frac{1}{14} + \frac{(35-40)^2}{28{,}750 - (560)^2/14}}$$

$= (10.507)\sqrt{0.0754} = 2.885$ (millions of dollars)

The estimated interval is 47.9 ± (2.179)(2.885) = 47.9 ± 6.286, or from $41.614 million to $54.186 million.

d. $$s_{IND} = s_{Y.X}\sqrt{1 + \frac{1}{14} + \frac{(35-40)^2}{28{,}750 - (560)^2/14}}$$

$= (10.507)\sqrt{1.7054} = 10.896$

The estimated interval is 47.9 ± (2.179)(10.896) = 47.9 ± 23.742, or from $24.158 million to $71.642 million.

e. The interval estimated in part (d) is much wider than that estimated in part (c). Individual values of Y cannot be predicted with as much precision as a conditional mean, because s_{IND} was used in part (d).

Exercise 9.8

1. a. $$s_{Y.X} = \sqrt{\frac{\Sigma(Y-\hat{Y})^2}{n-2}} = \sqrt{\frac{2{,}025}{46}}$$

$= 6.635$ (millions of dollars)

The standard error of estimate $s_{Y.X}$ measures the scatter of the observed values of Y (company sales) around the corresponding computed $\hat{Y}$ values on the regression line $\hat{Y} = 1.2 + 0.416X$.

b. $r^2 = 1 - \frac{\sum(Y-\hat{Y})^2}{\sum(Y-\overline{Y})^2} = 1 - \frac{2,025}{17,500} = 0.884$

$r_c^2 = 1 - \frac{\sum(Y-\hat{Y})^2/(n-2)}{\sum(Y-\overline{Y})^2/(n-1)} = 1 - \frac{2,025/46}{17,500/47} = 0.882$

The coefficient of determination is a measure of the degree of association between Y and X. The calculated figures may be interpreted as the percentage of variation in the dependent variable Y that has been accounted for, or "explained," by the variable X through a linear regression.

c. An appropriate hypothesis-testing procedure follows:

H_0: B = 0

H_1: B $\neq$ 0

The standard error of the regression coefficient is

$$s_b = \frac{s_{y.x}}{\sqrt{\sum(X-\overline{X})^2}} = \frac{6.635}{\sqrt{12,800}} = 0.059$$

The t statistic is

$$t = \frac{b-B}{s_b} = \frac{0.416-0}{0.059} = 7.051 \text{ with 46 degrees of freedom}$$

Since 7.051 > 2.704 (ν = 40), we reject at the 1% level of significance the null hypothesis that the population coefficient is equal to zero. We conclude the estimated relationship between company sales and operating expenses is significant.

2. a. $r_c^2 = 1 - \frac{s_{Y.X}^2}{s_Y^2} = 1 - \frac{0.04}{1.00} = 0.96$

$r_c = \sqrt{0.96} = 0.980$

The use of r values gives the impression of a stronger relationship than is actually present. Moreover, the use of r^2 is convenient because it can be interpreted as a percentage of variability explained by the regression equation.

b. $s_b = \frac{s_{Y.X}}{\sqrt{\sum(X-\overline{X})^2}} = \frac{0.2}{\sqrt{0.816}} = 0.221$

$$t = \frac{b-B)}{s_b} = \frac{4.0-0}{0.221} = 18.10, \text{ with 60 degrees of freedom}$$

Since 18.10 > 2.660, we reject at the 1% level of significance the null hypothesis that the population regression coefficient is zero.

3. a. $b = \frac{0.4594-(20)(0.149)(0.135)}{0.5146-(20)(0.149)^2} = 0.8090$

a = 0.135 - (0.8090)(0.149) = 0.0145

$\hat{R}_i$ = 0.0145 + 0.8090R_m

Since a = (1 - β)R_F, we have 0.0145 = 1 - 0.8090)R_F,

$$R_F = \frac{0.0145}{0.1910} = 0.0759$$

b. $s_{Y.X} = \sqrt{\dfrac{0.4332 - (0.0145)(2.70) - (0.8090)(0.4594)}{18}} = 0.0353$

$s_Y = \sqrt{\dfrac{0.0689}{19}} = 0.0602$

$r_c^2 = 1 - \dfrac{(0.0353)^2}{(0.0602)^2} = 0.6562$

$r^2 = \dfrac{(0.0145)(2.70) + (0.8090)(0.4594) - 20(0.135)^2}{0.4332 - 20(0.135)^2} = 0.6740$

c. $s_b = \dfrac{0.0353}{\sqrt{0.07058}} = 0.1329$

$t = \dfrac{0.8090 - 1}{0.1329} = -1.437$, with 18 degrees of freedom

Since −1.437 > −2.878, we conclude that the estimate regression coefficient is not significantly different from one.

d. $s_{\hat{Y}} = 0.0353\sqrt{\dfrac{1}{20} + \dfrac{(0.091 - 0.140)^2}{0.5146 - (2.98)^2/20}} = 0.0110$

$R_i = 0.0145 + 0.8090(0.091) = 0.0881$

The estimated interval is 0.0881 ± (2.101)(0.0110), or from 0.0650 to 0.1112.

4. a. For two students whose studying time differed by one hour, the one who studied more would score an estimated 7.6 points higher.

$s_b = \dfrac{5.4}{\sqrt{196}} = 0.386$

$t = \dfrac{7.6 - 0}{0.386} = 19.689$, with 60 degrees of freedom

Since 19.689 > 2.66, we conclude that the estimated coefficient is significantly different from zero at the 1% level of significance.

b. $r_c^2 = 1 - \dfrac{(5.4)^2}{(8.2)^2} = 0.566$

c. $s_{IND} = (5.4)\sqrt{1 + \dfrac{1}{62} + \dfrac{(1)^2}{196}} = (5.4)\sqrt{1.02123} = 5.457$

An estimated 95% prediction interval for the test score for a student who studied nine hours would be 74.8 ± (2)(5.457), or from about 63.9 to 85.7. Since this student's score is considerably below the lower limit of this interval, we may conclude that he is a poor performer.

5. a. $s_{Y.X} = \sqrt{\dfrac{\Sigma(Y - \hat{Y})^2}{n - 2}} = \sqrt{\dfrac{2000}{40}} = 7.071$

The standard error of estimate, $s_{Y.X}$, measures the scatter of the observed values of Y (company profits) around the corresponding computed $\hat{Y}$ values on the regression line, $\hat{Y} = 2.0 + 0.15X$.

b. $r^2 = 1 - \dfrac{\Sigma(Y - \hat{Y})^2}{\Sigma(Y - \hat{Y})^2} = 1 - \dfrac{2000}{17,000} = 0.882$

$r_c^2 = 1 \dfrac{\Sigma(Y - \overline{Y})^2/(n - 2)}{\Sigma(Y - \overline{Y})^2/(n - 1)} = 1 - \dfrac{2000/40}{17,000/41} = 0.879$

The coefficient of determination is a measure of the degree of association between Y and X. The calculated figures may be interpreted as the percentage of variation in the dependent variable, Y, that has been accounted for or "explained" by the relationship between Y and X expressed in the regression line.

c. An appropriate test is an hypothesis-testing procedure with the following null and alternative hypotheses:

H_0: $B = 0$

H_1: $B \neq 0$

The standard error of the regression coefficient is

$$s_b = \frac{s_{Y.X}}{\sqrt{\Sigma(X-\bar{X}^2}} = \frac{7.071}{\sqrt{500,000}} = 0.01$$

The t statistic is

$$t = \frac{b-B}{s_b} = \frac{0.15-0}{0.01} = 15 \text{ with 40 degrees of freedom}$$

Since 15 > 2.704, we reject at the 1% level of significance the null hypothesis that the population coefficient is equal to 0. We conclude that the estimated relationship between company profits and company asset size is significant.

6. a. $r_c^2 = 1 - \frac{8}{25} = 0.68$

b. The regression coefficient -0.01 indicates an inverse relationship between checking-account balance and bad checks written on the account. For every $100 increase in the checking-account balance, one *fewer* bad check is expected to be written on the account.

c. $t = \frac{0.82}{\sqrt{0.32/198}} = 20.4$

The critical t value at 5% for df = 198 is approximately 1.96. Since 20.4 is far in excess of 1.96, we reject H_0 and conclude that a linear relationship exists for all checking account balances and the number of bad checks written.

7. a. $b = \frac{147.5 - [(25)(2)(3)]}{102 - [25(2)^2]} = -1.25$

$a = 3 - [(-1.25)(2)] = 5.5$

$$s_{Y.X} = \sqrt{\frac{229 - [(5.5)(75)] - [(-1.25)(147.5)]}{23}} = 0.195$$

b. $s_b = \frac{0.195}{\sqrt{2}} = 0.138$

95% confidence interval for B:

-125 ± (2.069)(0.138), or from -1.536 to -0.964

df = 23

c. Since 0 is not within the 95% confidence interval computed in (b), we reject H_0 and conclude that b is significantly different from 0.

CHAPTER 10

Exercises 10.13

1. a. For b_1, $t_1 = \dfrac{(0.088 - 0)}{0.006} = 14.667$, with 120 degrees of freedom. Conclude that b_1 is significantly different from zero.

   For b_2, $t_2 = \dfrac{(0.065 - 0}{0.055} = 1.182$, with 120 degrees of freedom. Conclude that b_2 is not significantly different from zero.

   b. Family income (X_1) has a statistically significant effect on the number of cars owned (Y). However, after this income effect has been accounted for, family size (X_2) does not have a statistically significant influence.

   c. First, an increment of one unit in X_1 results in an increase of b_1 units in $\hat{Y}$, regardless of the values of other independent variables. Second, the inclusion of other independent variables "nets out" the effects of these variables; the net regression coefficient b_1 then will represent the effects of X_1 and any other variables that may be correlated with X_1 but not explicitly included in the analysis.

   d. $R_c^2 = 1 - \dfrac{419.384/120}{1,636.036/122} = 0.739$

   Approximately 74% of the variance of Y is explained by the regression equation relating Y to X_1 and X_2.

   e. $\hat{Y} = 0.570 + (0.088)(12) + (0.065)(6) = 2.016$ cars

   f. $F = \dfrac{1,216.652/2}{419.384/120} = 174.063$, with (2, 120) degrees of freedom. The regression is significant at the 1% level of significance.

2. a. The b_1 coefficient (5.8) indicates that if a firm spends $1 million more on research and development than another firm, and the two firms spend the same amount on advertising, then the estimated annual sales for the first firm will be $5.8 million more than the second firm's annual sales.

   b. H_0: $B_1 = 0$
   H_1: $B_1 \neq 0$

   $$t_1 = \frac{b_1 - 0}{s_{b_1}} = \frac{5.8}{1.20} = 4.83, \text{ with 19 degrees of freedom}$$

   Since 4.83 > 2.861, we reject H_0 at the 1% level of significance and conclude that b_1 is significantly different from zero.

H_0: $B_2 = 0$
H_1: $B_2 \neq 0$

$$t_2 = \frac{b_2 - 0}{s_{b_2}} = \frac{4.2}{1.31} = 3.21, \text{ with 19 degrees of freedom}$$

Since 3.21 > 2.861, we reject H_0 and conclude that b_2 is significantly different from zero at the 1% level of significance.

H_0: $B_3 = 0$
H_1: $B_3 \neq 0$

$$t_3 = \frac{b_3 - 0}{s_{b_3}} = \frac{7.4}{1.56} = 4.74, \text{ with 19 degrees of freedom}$$

Since 4.74 > 2.861, we reject H_0 and conclude that b_1 is significantly different from zero at the 1% level of significance.

c. If multicollinearity exists, that is, if the independent variables are highly correlated, the estimated regression coefficients for these variables tend to be unreliable. Separating the individual influences of the variables becomes extremely difficult.

d. $R_c^2 = 1 - \dfrac{S_{Y.12}^2}{s_Y^2} = 1 - \dfrac{(12.4)^2}{(25)^2} = 0.754$

e. $\hat{Y} = -2.3 + 5.8(6) + 4.2(10) + 7.4(7) = 126.3$ (millions of dollars)

f. $\beta_1 = b_1 \dfrac{s_{X_1}}{s_Y} = (5.8)\dfrac{(15)}{25} = 3.48$

$\beta_2 = b_2 \dfrac{s_{X_2}}{s_Y} = (4.2)\dfrac{(10)}{25} = 1.68$

$\beta_3 = b_3 \dfrac{s_{X_3}}{s_Y} = (7.4)\dfrac{(5)}{25} = 1.48$

β_1 measures the number of standard deviations by which $\hat{Y}$ changes with each change of one standard deviation in X_1.

3. a. $S_{Y.12} = \sqrt{28/(21-3)} = 1.247\%$

See page 523 for the assumptions for using this measure. There are 18 degrees of freedom.

b. $R_c^2 = 1 - \dfrac{28/18}{120/20} = 0.741$

c. $s_{b_1} = \dfrac{1.247}{\sqrt{(800{,}000)(0.2775)}} = 0.00265$

$s_{b_2} = \dfrac{1.247}{\sqrt{(100)(0.2775)}} = 0.237$

H_0: $B_1 = 0$
H_1: $B_1 \neq 0$
H_0: $B_2 = 0$
H_1: $B_2 \neq 0$

For b_1, $t_1 = -0.003/0.00265 = -1.13$, with 18 degrees of freedom. Conclude that b_1 does not differ significantly from zero at the 1% level of significance. For b_2, $t_2 = -4/0.237 = -16.878$, with 18 degrees of freedom. Conclude that b_2 differs significantly from zero at the 1% level of significance.

d. $\hat{Y}$ = 17 - (0.003)(200) - (4)(2.00) = 8.4% unemployed

e. In this case, $F = \dfrac{92/2}{28/18} = 29.57$, with (2, 18) degrees of freedom.

The regression is significant at the 1% level of significance.

4. a. The value $b_2 = 0.8$ indicates that if an option's expiration date is one month farther away than another option, and the underlying stocks have the same price volatility, then the estimated value of the first option exceeds that of the second by $0.80.

b. The reliability of the individual net regression coefficients is particularly important if the purpose of the analysis is to measure the separate effects of the independent variables on the dependent variable.

c. $$S_{Y.12} = \sqrt{\frac{\Sigma(Y-\hat{Y})^2}{n-k}} = \sqrt{\frac{236}{40}} = \$2.429$$

d. $$R_c^2 = 1 - \frac{S_{Y.12}^2}{s_Y^2} = 1 - \frac{(2.429)^2}{17.643} = 0.666$$

$$s_Y^2 = \frac{\Sigma(Y-\overline{Y})^2}{n-1} = \frac{741}{42} = 17.643$$

e. $\hat{Y}$ = 3.0 + (0.3)(20) + (0.8)(6) = $13.80

f. H_0: The regression is not significant
H_1: The regression is significant

$$F = \frac{\Sigma(\hat{Y}-\overline{Y})^2/(k-1)}{\Sigma(Y-\hat{Y})^2/(n-k)} = \frac{622/2}{236/40} = 52.71$$

Since 52.71 > 5.18, we reject the null hypothesis that the regression is not significant at the 1% level of significance.

5. a. $$r_c^2 = 1 - \frac{3^2}{8^2} = 0.859$$

b. $t_1 = \dfrac{0.031}{0.008} = 3.875$, with 14 degrees of freedom

Conclude that b_1 differs significantly from zero at the 1% level of significance.

c. $$R_c^2 = 1 - \frac{(2.6)^2}{8^2} = 0.894$$

The inclusion of X_2 has explained relatively little of the variance in Y beyond that already explained by X_1 alone.

d. The value $b_1 = 0.030$ indicates that if a student scores one point higher on the GMAT than another student with the same amount of work experience, then the estimated starting salary of the first exceeds that of the second by $30.

e. For b_1, $t_1 = 0.030/0.009 = 3.333$, with 13 degrees of freedom. Conclude that b_1 is significantly different from zero at the 1% level of significance. For b_2, $t_2 = 1.05/0.75 = 1.4$, with 13 degrees of freedom. Conclude that b_2 is not significantly different from zero.

We conclude that the GMAT score has a statistically significant effect on starting salary, but after this GMAT effect has been accounted for, the numbers of years of work experience is not statistically significant. At least two situations are possible: (1) There is simply no relation between starting salary and work experience. (2) The two independent variables X_1 and X_2 are highly correlated, which would reduce the reliability of the estimated coefficients.

6. a. $t_1 = \dfrac{b_1 - 0}{s_{b_1}} = \dfrac{-0.25120}{0.03411} = -7.364$, with 30 degrees of freedom

Since $-7.364 < -2.750$, we reject the null hypothesis and conclude that b_1 differs significantly from zero at the 1% level of significance.

$t_2 = \dfrac{b_2 - 0}{s_{b_2}} = \dfrac{-0.03015}{0.00712} = -4.235$, with 30 degrees of freedom

Since $-4.235 < -2.750$, we reject H_0 and conclude that b_2 is significantly different from zero.

b. $S^2_{Y.12} = \dfrac{2.8712}{30} = 0.09571$

$s^2_Y = \dfrac{6.4224}{32} = 0.2007$

$R^2_c = 1 - \dfrac{s^2_{Y.12}}{s^2_Y} = 1 - \dfrac{0.09571}{0.2007} = 0.523$

$R_c = \sqrt{R^2_c} = 0.723$

R^2_c is easier to interpret, because it is a percentage figure and R is not.

c. $F = \dfrac{3.5512/2}{2.8712/30} = 18.553$, with (2,30) degrees of freedom

Since $18.553 > 5.39$, we reject H_0 and conclude that the regression is significant at the 1% level of significance.

$$F = \frac{\sum(\hat{Y} - \overline{Y})^2/(k-1)}{\sum(Y - \hat{Y})^2/(n-k)}$$

The F statistic compares the mean square due to regression (explained variance) to the residual mean square (unexplained variance).

7. a. A high degree of correlation is quite likely between each pair of independent variables. This result follows from the fact that large firms probably have large asset sizes, large stockholders' equity, and large net incomes, and small firms probably have smaller values for these three variables.

b. Variable X_3, which was highly collinear with the other two independent variables, was dropped.

c. From the statistics given, this procedure appears to have been effective. The increase in the F value, after taking degrees of freedom into account, probably indicates a more significant overall relationship. Also, the t values for the slope coefficients for variables X_1 and X_2 have improved.

REVIEW EXERCISES FOR CHAPTER 10

Note: The following scientific notation is used in the computer runs in these solutions: $E^{-1} = 10^{-1}$, $E^{0} = 10^{0}$, and so on.

1. a. Selected computer output

Variate Correlations (*r* values)

	GPA	V-SAT	M-SAT	RANK	C-SIZE
GPA	1.000	0.614	0.455	-0.400	-0.183
V-SAT		1.000	0.683	-0.199	-0.412
M-SAT			1.000	-0.108	-0.113
RANK				1.000	0.607
C-SIZE					1.000

Slope coefficients and standard errors

	COEFF.	ST.ERROR	*t*
Y-INTERCEPT	-2.1068611	1.3589553	-1.5504
V-SAT	0.099167706	0.037744292	2.6274
M-SAT	-0.0035895436	0.022859886	-0.1570
RANK	-0.013173221	0.0056250958	-2.3419
C-SIZE	0.0026004726	0.0015206651	1.7101

$\hat{Y} = -2.1069 + 0.0992(\text{V-SAT}) - 0.0036(\text{M-SAT}) - 0.0132(\text{RANK}) + 0.0026(\text{C-SIZE})$ (with rounding)

b. Estimated GPA increases by 0.0992 with each one-unit increase in V-SAT score. (Since the V-SAT and M-SAT scores are given in two digits rather than the conventional three digits, one unit of these scores is equivalent to 10 points). Estimated GPA decreases by 0.0036 with each one-unit increase in M-SAT score. Estimated GPA decreases by 0.0132 with each one-unit increase in RANK. Estimated GPA increases by 0.0026 with each increase of one person in class size.

c. $\nu = n - k = 20 - 5 = 15$ degrees of freedom

$t_{0.05,15} = |2.131|$

Therefore, the slope coefficients for V-SAT and RANK are significant at the 5% level.

d. The sign for V-SAT makes sense, because GPA would be expected to vary directly with V-SAT scores. An inverse relationship does not seem reasonable between GPA and M-SAT scores. However, the slope coefficient does not differ significantly from zero. An inverse relationship between GPA and RANK is reasonable (one is the highest rank). The data indicate a direct relationship between GPA and C-SIZE. However, the slope coefficient does not differ significantly from zero.

e.

Analysis of variance table

EFFECTS	SUM OF SQUARES	DEGREES OF FREEDOM	MEAN SUM OF SQUARES	F
REGRESSION	6.5465705	4	1.6366426	4.56849
ERROR	5.3736845	15	0.35824563	
TOTAL	11.9202550	19		

Since F = 4.56849 > $F_{0.05;4,15}$ = 3.06, reject the null hypothesis of no relationship between the dependent variable and the independent variables.

f. R^2 = 0.549197, uncorrected for degrees of freedom. About 54.9% of the variation in freshman grade point averages has been accounted for by the regression equation relating GPA to verbal SAT scores, mathematics SAT scores, class rank, and class size.

g. The correlation coefficient for V-SAT and M-SAT is 0.683, which suggests multicollinearity between these two variables. Not surprisingly, the slope coefficient for at least one of these variables is insignificant.

2. a.

Selected computer output

Variate correlations (r values)

	GPA	V-SAT	RANK/C-SIZE
GPA	1.000	0.614	-0.483
V-SAT		1.000	0.023
RANK/C-SIZE			1.000

Slope coefficients and standard errors

	COEFF.	ST.ERROR	t
Y-INTERCEPT	-1.1660702	0.97660667	-1.194
V-SAT	0.087295002	0.02071934	4.21321
RANK/C-SIZE	-2.8664136	0.85566342	-3.34993

$\hat{Y}$ = -1.1661 + 0.0873(V-SAT) - 2.8664(RANK/C-SIZE)

b. The interpretations of slope coefficients are similar to those in exercise 1.

$\nu = n - k = 20 - 3 = 17$

$t_{0.05,17} = |2.110|$

Therefore, the slope coefficients for V-SAT and RANK/C-SIZE are significant at the 5% level.

The signs of both slope coefficients are reasonable.

Analysis of variance table

	SUM OF SQUARES	DEGREES OF FREEDOM	MEAN SUM OF SQUARES	F
REGRESSION	7.4504564	2	3.7252282	14.1682
ERROR	4.4697986	17	0.26292933	
TOTAL	11.9202550	19		

Since F = 14.1682 > $F_{0.05;2,17}$ = 3.59, reject the null hypothesis of no relationship between the dependent variable and the independent variables.

R^2 = 0.625025, uncorrected for degrees of freedom

c. The revised model that includes only two independent variables, V-SAT and RANK/C-SIZE, explains more of the variation in freshman GPA (R^2 = 0.625) than does the first model (R^2 = 0.549). V-SAT is the one variable most highly correlated with freshman grade point averages. Note that since the revised model only accounts for 62.5% of the variation in freshman grade point averages, other factors not included in the regression equation have a substantial effect on freshman grade point averages.

3. a. Selected computer output

Variate Correlations (r values)

	W-L	BA	ERA	SB	R	H	HR
W-L	1.000	0.577	-0.756	0.281	0.783	0.543	0.631
BA		1.000	-0.239	-0.001	0.807	0.975	0.378
ERA			1.000	-0.414	-0.361	-0.241	-0.286
SB				1.000	0.116	-0.066	-0.152
R					1.000	0.784	0.686
H						1.000	0.335
HR							1.000

Slope coefficients and standard errors

	COEFF.	ST.ERROR	t
Y-INTERCEPT	$3.216E^{-1}$	0.28802552	1.1167
BA	$3.330E^{0}$	3.3560615	0.9923
ERA	$-1.059E^{-1}$	0.018482928	-5.7292
SB	$-4.620E^{-5}$	0.00017998154	-0.2567
R	$6.245E^{-4}$	0.00024166995	2.5842
H	$-5.168E^{-4}$	0.00048945171	-1.0560
HR	$2.235E^{-4}$	0.00038283056	0.5837

b. $\nu = n - k = 26 - 7 = 19$

$t_{0.05,19} = |2.093|$

Therefore, the slope coefficients for earned run average and runs scored are significant at the 5% level.

c.

Analysis of variance table

EFFECTS	SUM OF SQUARES	DEGREES OF FREEDOM	MEAN SUM OF SQUARES	F
REGRESSION	$1.250E^{-1}$	6	$2.084E^{-2}$	25.1409
ERROR	$1.575E^{-2}$	19	$8.288E^{-4}$	
TOTAL	$1.408E^{-1}$	25		

Since $F = 25.1409 > F_{0.01;6,19} = 3.94$, reject the hypothesis of no relationship between the dependent variable and the independent variables.

d. $R^2 = 0.888$
About 88.8% of the variation in win-loss percentages has been accounted for by the regression equation.

e.

Selected computer output

Variate Correlations (r values)

	W-L	ERA	SB	R
W-L	1.000	-0.756	0.281	0.783
ERA		1.000	-0.414	-0.361
SB			1.000	0.116
R				1.000

Slope Coefficients and Standard Errors

	COEFF.	ST.ERROR	t
Y-INTERCEPT	$4.520E^{-1}$	0.10733014	4.2112
ERA	$-1.050E^{-1}$	0.017108997	-6.1396
SB	$-2.465E^{-5}$	0.0001346113	-0.1831
R	$-6.590E^{-4}$	0.0000923099	7.1387

f. The second model, which used only three independent variables—earned run average, stolen bases, and runs—accounted for almost as much variation in win-loss percentage as did the first model that used six independent variables ($R^2 = 0.871$ vs. $R^2 = 0.888$). The slope coefficient for stolen bases was not significant in the model with three independent variables. Therefore, earned run average and runs scored were the most significant variables in explaining differences in win-loss percentages of major league teams. As expected, a good deal of multicollinearity existed among batting averages, hits, and runs scored. Since earned run average is a defensive variable and runs scored is an offensive variable, the results indicate that teams with the best defenses and offenses tended to have the highest win-loss percentages. Analogously, teams with the worst defenses and offenses tended to lose the most games.

CHAPTER 11

Exercises 11.4

Note: **Minitab was used in these solutions for the fitting of trend equations and associated output. Selected output from the REGRESS command is given in most instances.**

1. a. **See section 11.2.**
   b. **The cyclical component of a time series may be depicted in terms of relative cyclical residuals or percentage of trend.**

2. a.

```
MTB > BRIEF 3
MTB > REGRESS C3 ON 1 PREDICTOR C2, C4 C5

THE REGRESSION EQUATION IS
GSERVCON = 1246 + 41.2 TIME

PREDICTOR          COEF          STDEV        T-RATIO          P
CONSTANT        1245.90          12.43         100.21      0.000
TIME             41.181          1.460          28.20      0.000

S = 22.02    R-SQ = 98.5%    R-SQ (ADJ) = 98.4%
```

   b.

```
MTB > PRINT C1 C2 C3 C5 C6
```

ROW	YEAR	TIME	GSERVCON	TREND	%TREND
1	1975	1	1286.4	1287.08	99.947
2	1976	2	1324.4	1328.26	99.709
3	1977	3	1368.7	1369.44	99.946
4	1978	4	1426.9	1410.62	101.154
5	1979	5	1478.6	1451.80	101.846
6	1980	6	1511.1	1492.99	101.213
7	1981	7	1533.4	1534.17	99.950
8	1982	8	1547.5	1575.35	98.232
9	1983	9	1585.5	1616.53	98.081
10	1984	10	1625.2	1657.71	98.039
11	1985	11	1684.3	1698.89	99.141
12	1986	12	1738.1	1740.07	99.887
13	1987	13	1801.1	1781.25	101.114
14	1988	14	1855.4	1822.43	101.809

The original annual series contains trend, cyclical, and irregular factors. The percentage of trend series contains only cyclical and irregular factors, since the division by trend eliminates that factor.

c. **See figure: Straight-line trend fitted to GNP-services in 1982 constant dollars in the United States, 1975-1988.**

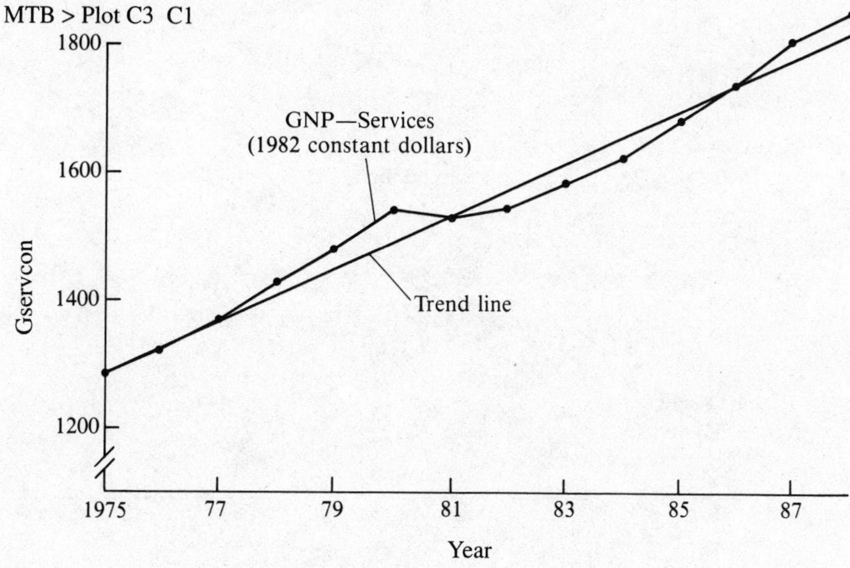

3. MTB > BRIEF 3

```
MTB > NAME C5 'TREND' C6 '%TREND'
MTB > REGRESS C3 1 C2 C4 C5

THE REGRESSION EQUATION IS
GSERVCUR = 491 + 136 TIME
```

PREDICTOR	COEF	STDEV	T-RATIO	P
CONSTANT	490.77	27.90	17.59	0.000
TIME	135.846	3.277	41.45	0.000

S = 49.43   R-SQ = 99.3%   R-SQ (ADJ) = 99.2%

ROW	YEAR	TIME	GSERVCUR	TREND	%TREND
1	1975	1	725.2	626.61	115.733
2	1976	2	803.5	762.46	105.383
3	1977	3	895.9	898.31	99.732
4	1978	4	1003.0	1034.15	96.988
5	1979	5	1121.9	1170.00	95.889
6	1980	6	1265.0	1305.85	96.872
7	1981	7	1415.4	1441.69	98.176
8	1982	8	1547.5	1577.54	98.096
9	1983	9	1682.5	1713.38	98.198
10	1984	10	1813.9	1849.23	98.090
11	1985	11	1968.3	1985.08	99.155
12	1986	12	2118.4	2120.92	99.881
13	1987	13	2295.7	2256.77	101.725
14	1988	14	2478.4	2392.61	103.585

See figure: Straight-line trend fitted to GNP-Services in current dollars in the United States, 1975-1988.

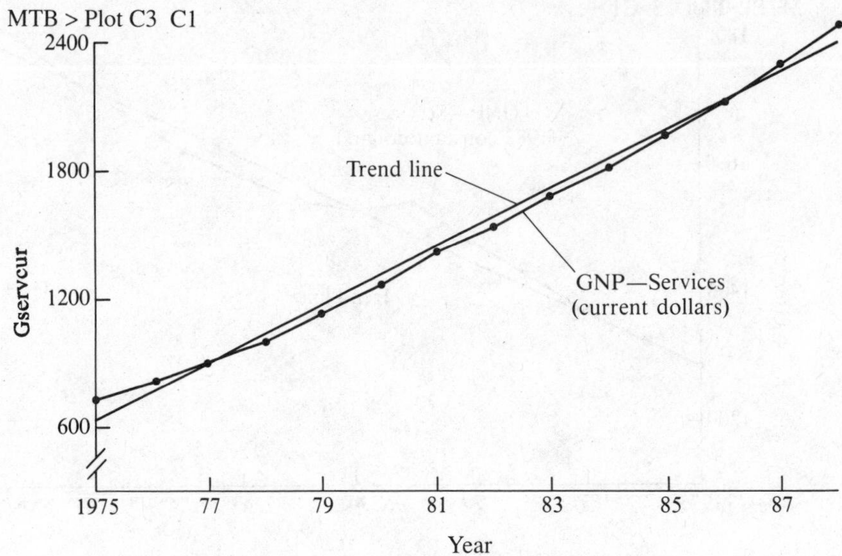

The trend line for the 1982 constant-dollar series seems to fit the data more closely, since that series has relatively more constant annual amounts of change than does the current-dollar series.

4.

ROW	YEAR	TIME	PURCHASES
1	1980	1	246.9
2	1981	2	259.6
3	1982	3	272.7
4	1983	4	275.1
5	1984	5	290.8
6	1985	6	326.0
7	1986	7	333.4
8	1987	8	339.0
9	1988	9	326.1

```
MTB > REGRESS C3 1 C2;
SUBC> PREDICT C4.
```

THE REGRESSION EQUATION IS
PURCHASE = 236 + 12.1 TIME

PREDICTOR	COEF	STDEV	T-RATIO	P
CONSTANT	236.014	8.581	27.50	0.000
TIME	12.122	1.525	7.95	0.000

S = 11.81   R-SQ = 90.0%   R-SQ(ADJ) = 88.6%

YEAR	PROJECTED FIGURE (BILLIONS OF 1982 DOLLARS)
1990	357.23
1991	369.35
1992	381.47
1993	393.60
1994	405.72
1995	417.84

5. a. $\frac{222-123}{5}$ = 19.8 billion persons per decade

b. $\hat{Y}_t = 94.93 + 21.22t$

t = 1 in 1930

t is in ten-year intervals

Y is in billions of persons

c. The answer to part (a) and the slope of the straight line fitted to the original data (19.8 and 21.22) differ by about 7%. The results are consistent. The 19.8 figure is the average increase from the earliest population figure in 1930 to the latest one in 1980. The 21.22 figure is the slope of the line; it takes all of the original data into account.

... = 211.6

...dual = 214 − 211.6 = 2.4 billion

...dual = $\frac{214-211.6}{211.6}(100) = 1.1\%$

... was 2.4 billion, or 1.1%, above the trend level ...d irregular factors.

...s county is increasing by decreasing amounts and ...tage rate.

... $- 0.52(16)^2 = 179.01$ (thousands)

...0 from the computed trend figure of 179,010 does ...a poor fit. Possibly, the fit is adequate and the ...n unusually strong cyclical influence.


```
... C4 C5

...N IS
...TIME

...          COEF          STDEV      T-RATIO        P
...          1530         0.7420         4.25    0.001
...         28591        0.06508         4.39    0.000

....2%   R-SQ(ADJ) = 50.4%

MTB > LET C4 = 100*((C2-C5)/C5)
MTB > NAME C4 'RCRPRIME'
MTB > REGRESS C3 1 C1 C5 C6

THE REGRESSION EQUATION IS
BOND = 3.63 + 0.310 TIME

PREDICTOR          COEF          STDEV      T-RATIO        P
CONSTANT         3.6319         0.2632        13.80    0.000
TIME            0.31033        0.02308        13.44    0.000

S = 0.5511   R-SQ = 91.4%   R-SQ(ADJ) = 90.9%
```

b. MTB > LET C5=100*((C3-C6)/C6)
MTB > NAME C5 'RCRBOND'

MTB > PRINT C1 C2 C3 C4 C5

ROW	TIME	PRIME	BOND	RCRPRIME	RCRBOND
1	1	2.97	4.35	-13.6350%	10.3427%
2	2	3.26	4.33	-12.4787%	1.8201%
3	3	3.55	4.26	-11.4872	-6.6389
4	4	3.97	4.40	-7.6020	-9.7114
5	5	4.38	4.49	-4.4199	-13.3806
6	6	5.55	5.13	13.9992	-6.6242
7	7	5.10	5.51	-1.0548	-5.0698
8	8	5.90	6.18	8.4503	1.0696
9	9	7.83	7.03	36.7401	9.4175
10	10	7.72	8.04	28.4076	19.3717
11	11	5.11	7.39	-18.8634	4.8882
12	12	4.69	7.21	-28.7659	-1.9838
13	13	8.15	7.44	18.6345	-2.9514
14	14	9.87	8.57	37.9310	7.4393
15	15	6.33	8.83	-14.9384	6.5533
16	16	5.35	8.43	-30.7674	-1.9455
17	17	5.60	8.02	-30.1178	-9.9645
18	18	7.99	8.73	-3.7280	-5.2933
19	19	10.91	9.63	27.0774	1.0677

Conclusion: **Short-term prime commercial paper interest rates display greater cyclical fluctuations than long-term corporate bonds interest rates.**

8. a. MTB > PRINT C1-C3

ROW	YEAR	TIME	EXPENSE
1	1975	1	235.2
2	1976	2	254.9
3	1977	3	273.2
4	1978	4	301.3
5	1979	5	327.7
6	1980	6	363.2
7	1981	7	391.4
8	1982	8	414.3
9	1983	9	440.2
10	1984	10	475.9
11	1985	11	516.7
12	1986	12	561.9
13	1987	13	602.8
14	1988	14	646.6

MTB > NAME C4 'TREND1' NAME C5 'TREND2'
MTB > REGRESS C3 1 C2 C6 C4

THE REGRESSION EQUATION IS
EXPENSE = 179 + 31.4 TIME

PREDICTOR	COEF	STDEV	T-RATIO	P
CONSTANT	179.344	9.023	19.88	0.000
TIME	31.376	1.060	29.61	0.000

S = 15.98   R-SQ = 98.6%   R-SQ(ADJ) = 98.5%

b.
```
MTB > NAME C7 'TIMETIME'
MTB > LET C7=C2**2
MTB > REGRESS C3 2 C2 C7 C6 C5

THE REGRESSION EQUATION IS
EXPENSE = 218 + 16.8 TIME + 0.971 TIMETIME
```

PREDICTOR	COEF	STDEV	T-RATIO	P
CONSTANT	218.193	5.014	43.52	0.000
TIME	16.808	1.538	10.93	0.000
TIMETIME	0.97122	0.09972	9.74	0.000

```
S = 5.381    R-SQ = 99.9%    R-SQ(ADJ) = 99.8%
```

c.
```
MTB > NAME C4 '%TREND1' C5 '%TREND2'
MTB > LET C4=100*(C3/C4)
MTB > LET C5=100*(C3/C5)
MTB > PRINT C1 C2 C3 C4 C5
```

ROW	YEAR	TIME	EXPENSE	%TREND1	%TREND2
1	1975	1	235.2	111.617	99.673
2	1976	2	254.9	105.289	99.690
3	1977	3	273.2	99.901	98.501
4	1978	4	301.3	98.836	100.112
5	1979	5	327.7	97.465	100.364
6	1980	6	363.2	98.803	102.598
7	1981	7	391.4	98.101	102.077
8	1982	8	414.3	96.270	99.876
9	1983	9	440.2	95.337	98.230
10	1984	10	475.9	96.511	98.450
11	1985	11	516.7	98.517	99.252
12	1986	12	561.9	101.087	100.386
13	1987	13	602.8	102.651	100.328
14	1988	14	646.6	104.525	100.426

The second-degree trend line appears to lie closer to the actual data.

Exercises 11.5

1. a. 429,000. The number of passengers in December would tend to be closer to 429,000 because the trend value of 325,000 does not account for seasonal variations. With a December seasonal index of 132, the number of passengers would tend to lie above the trend figure, in the absence of cyclical and random factors.

   b. $\frac{Y}{SI} \times 100 = \frac{415,000}{132} \times 100 = 314,394$

   $\frac{Y/SI}{\hat{Y}_t} = \frac{314,394}{325,000} = 96.7\%$ of trend

   c. The trend value for December 1991 indicates the level of sales for that month if cyclical, seasonal, and random factors had not been present.

2. a.

Quarter	Y/SI (thousands of gallons)
Spring	28,333
Summer	25,500
Fall	24,500
Winter	25,200

The deseasonalized sales volumes are quite close to 25,000,000 gallons except for the spring quarter of 1990. Cyclical and random fluctuations are quite large for the spring quarter of 1990.

b. Quarterly sales volume for 1991 = 1.15 × 25,000,000 gallons per quarter = 28,750,000 gallons per quarter.

Quarter	$\hat{Y}_t \times SI$ Sales Forecast (gallons)
Spring	25,875,00
Summer	35,937,500
Fall	30,187,500
Winter	23,000,000

3. a. Seasonal variations have to be removed from the actual sales volumes by dividing the latter figures by the seasonal indices. These values will indicate whether a decline not attributable to seasonal variations had occurred.

Month	Fresh Milk Sales Volume, Deseasonalized (thousands of gallons)
July 1990	15,000
August 1990	15,753
September 1990	16,332

If seasonal variations are removed, an increasing trend in sales volumes of fresh milk is seen, contrary to the observations of the vice-president of marketing.

b. Actual sales volume is divided by the seasonal indices to remove seasonal variations. These deseasonalized (Y/SI) values are then divided by a series of trend figures. To obtain the trend values, we need more data on milk sales volume for months of earlier years. We could compute a trend line from these data to yield trend values. The deseasonalized figures divided by the trend values would reflect primarily the effect of cyclical fluctuations, since trend and seasonal influences have been removed.

4. a. (1) June
(2) May

b. April

c. In the multiplicative model of time-series analysis, the original monthly figures consist of the product of the trend level, the cyclical relative (combined effect of cyclical and irregular factor), and the seasonal index. In symbols,

$$Y = \hat{Y}_t\left(\frac{Y/SI}{\hat{Y}_t}\right)(SI)$$

For March 1990:

$\hat{Y}_t = 641.04 + 0.96(63) = 701.5$

$\dfrac{Y}{SI} = \dfrac{570}{0.86} = 662.8$

$\dfrac{Y/SI}{\hat{Y}_t} = \dfrac{662.8}{701.5} = 0.945$

$SI = 0.86$

The equation 570 = (701.5)(0.945)(0.86) represents the breakdown of the March 1990 figure into its components.

If an additive model were used—that is, $Y = T + (C + I) + S$—then the breakdown would be as follows:

$\hat{Y}_t = 701.5$

Since $Y/SI = 662.8$, the effect of the seasonal factor is 570.0 - 662.8 = -92.8. The effects of the cyclical and irregular factors are measured by the absolute cyclical residual

$Y/SI - \hat{Y}_t - 662.8 - 701.5 = -38.7$

In summary, the breakdown of components of the March 1990 figure using the additive model is as follows:

Trend	701.5
Seasonal	- 92.8
	608.7
Cyclical and Irregular	- 38.7
Original	570.0

5. a. Total of modified means = 400.38
Adjustment factor = 400/400.38 = 0.9991
The seasonal indices are 93.34 (I), 97.36 (II), 107.31 (III), and 101.99 (IV).

b. Yes, constant seasonal indices seem appropriate, because the percentage of moving average figures are relatively stable for each quarter.

c. See column 7 of the table.

d. There is some evidence of cycles. Cyclical peaks appear in 1986, quarter II and 1989, quarter II, with corresponding cyclical troughs in 1987, quarter III and 1990, quarter I.

Complete table of values (solution to exercise 5(c))

(1) Quarter	(2) Number of Autos Sold	(3) Four Quarter Moving Total	(4) Two-of-a-Four-Quarter Moving Total	(5) Moving Average Col. 5 = Col. 4 × $\frac{1}{8}$	(6) Original Data as Percentage of Moving Average	(7) Adjusted Sales Figures
1985						
I	362					387.83
II	386					396.47
III	437	1,612	3,267	408.38	107.01	407.23
IV	427	1,655	3,357	419.63	101.76	418.67
1986						
I	405	1,702	3,437	429.63	94.27	433.90
II	433	1,735	3,486	435.75	99.37	444.74
III	470	1,751	3,499	437.38	107.46	437.98
IV	443	1,748	3,483	435.38	101.75	434.36
1987						
I	402	1,735	3,456	432.00	93.06	430.68
II	420	1,721	3,439	429.88	97.70	431.39
III	456	1,718	3,450	431.25	105.74	424.94
IV	440	1,732	3,484	435.50	101.03	431.41
1988						
I	416	1,752	3,556	444.50	93.59	445.68
II	440	1,804	3,660	457.50	96.17	451.93
III	508	1,856	3,751	468.88	108.34	473.39
IV	492	1,895	3,830	478.75	102.77	482.40
1989						
I	455	1,935	3,887	485.88	93.64	487.47
II	480	1,952	3,910	488.75	98.21	493.02
III	525	1,958	3,897	487.13	107.77	389.24
IV	498	1,939	3,870	483.75	102.95	488.28
1990						
I	436	1,931	3,873	484.13	90.06	467.11
II	472	1,942	3,915	489.38	96.45	484.80
III	536	1,973				499.49
IV	529					518.68

Percentage of Moving Averages (quarters)

Year	I	II	III	IV
1985			107.01	101.76
1986	~~94.27~~	~~99.37~~	107.46	101.75
1987	93.06	97.70	~~105.74~~	~~101.03~~
1988	93.59	~~96.17~~	~~108.34~~	102.77
1989	93.64	98.21	107.77	~~102.95~~
1990	~~90.06~~	96.45		
Modified Means	93.43	97.45	107.41	102.09

Quarter	Percentage of Trend $\frac{Y/SI}{\hat{Y}_t} \times 100$	Quarter	Percentage of Trend $\frac{Y/SI}{Y_t} \times 100$
1985		1988	
I	96.96	I	96.89
II	97.89	II	97.19
III	99.32	III	100.72
IV	100.88	IV	101.56
1986		1989	
I	103.31	I	101.56
II	104.64	II	101.65
III	101.86	III	99.84
IV	99.85	IV	98.64
1987		1990	
I	97.88	I	93.42
II	96.94	II	96.00
III	94.43	III	97.94
IV	94.82	IV	98.92

6. a. $\frac{Y}{SI} = \frac{\$2.5}{1.10} = \$2.27$ million

$\hat{Y}_t = 1.85 + 0.16(3) + 0.03(3)^2$

$= \$2.60$ million

Relative cyclical residual $= \frac{2.27 - 2.6}{2.60}(100) = -12.7\%$

b. A relative cyclical residual of -12.7% indicates that the seasonally adjusted figure is 12.7% below the trend figure because of cyclical and irregular factors.

c. For December 1991:

$\hat{Y}_t = 1.85 + 0.16(4) + 0.03(4)^2$

$= 2.97$

$Y = (2.97)(1.10) = \$3.27$ million

7.

(1) Quarter	(2) Enroll-ment (tens)	(3) Four-Quarter Moving Total	(4) Two-of-a-Four-Quarter Moving Total	(5) Moving Average Col. 5 = Col. 4 × $\frac{1}{8}$	(6) Original Data as Percentage of Moving Average	(7) Adjusted Enroll-ment Figures (tens)
1986						
Fall	270					218.87
Winter	253					227.76
Spring	243	900	1,815	226.88	107.11	222.77
Summer	134	915	1,835	229.38	58.42	237.25
1987						
Fall	285	920	1,853	231.63	123.04	231.03
Winter	258	933	1,858	232.25	111.09	232.27
Spring	256	925	1,851	231.38	110.64	234.69
Summer	126	926	1,850	231.25	54.49	223.09
1988						
Fall	286	924	1,851	231.38	123.61	231.84
Winter	256	927	1,851	231.38	110.64	230.46
Spring	259	924	1,853	231.63	111.82	237.44
Summer	123	929	1,867	233.38	52.70	217.78
1989						
Fall	291	938	1,873	234.13	124.29	235.89
Winter	265	935	1,889	236.13	112.23	238.57
Spring	256	954	1,906	238.25	107.45	234.69
Summer	142	952	1,910	238.75	59.48	251.42
1990						
Fall	289	958	1,923	240.38	120.23	234.27
Winter	271	965	1,953	244.13	111.01	243.97
Spring	263	988				241.11
Summer	165					292.14

Percentage of Moving Averages

	Fall	Winter	Spring	Summer
1986			~~107.11~~	58.42
1987	123.04	111.09	110.64	54.49
1988	123.61	~~110.64~~	~~111.82~~	~~52.70~~
1989	~~124.29~~	~~112.23~~	107.45	~~59.48~~
1990	~~120.23~~	111.01		
Modified Means	123.33	111.05	109.05	56.46

Total of Modified means = 399.89
Adjustment factor = 400.00/399.89 = 1.0003
The seasonal indexes are 123.36 (Fall), 111.08 (Winter), 109.08 (Spring), and 56.48 (Summer).

8. a. (3)
b. (2)
c. (4)
d. (2)
e. (1)
f. (1)
g. (3)

Exercises 11.6

1.

Month	Next Forecast $w = 0.1$	Next Forecast $w = 0.6$
1	10 = F_2	10 = F_2
2	10 = F_3	10 = F_3
3	10 = F_4	10 = F_4
4	10.5 = F_5	13 = F_5
5	10.45 = F_6	11.2 = F_6
6	10.405 = F_7	10.48 = F_7
7	10.3645 = F_8	10.192 = F_8
8	10.32805 = F_9	10.0768 = F_9
9	10.295245 = F_{10}	10.03072 = F_{10}
10	10.265721 = F_{11}	10.012288 = F_{11}

2.

Month	Actual Demand	Next Forecast $w = 0.1$	Next Forecast $w = 0.6$
1	10 = A_1	10 = F_2	10 = F_2
2	10 = A_2	10 = F_3	10 = F_3
3	10 = A_3	10 = F_4	10 = F_4
4	10 = A_4	10.5 = F_5	13 = F_5
5	15 = A_5	10.95 = F_6	14.2 = F_6
6	15 = A_6	11.355 = F_7	14.68 = F_7
7	15 = A_7	11.7195 = F_8	14.872 = F_8
8	15 = A_8	12.04755 = F_9	14.9488 = F_9
9	15 = A_9	12.342795 = F_{10}	14.97952 = F_{10}
10	15 = A_{10}	12.608516 = F_{11}	14.991808 = F_{11}

3. Forecasts derived from low values of w tend to vary less from period to period than corresponding forecasts made with high w values. In exercise 1, when a one-time jump in demand to 15 in month 4 occurred, the $w = 0.1$ forecasts changed little from the basic level of 10. On the other hand, the forecasts using $w = 0.6$ increased sharply to a month 5 forecast of 13 and then dropped quickly to values close to the basic sales volume of 10 units. In exercise 2, the actual sales data shifted to a higher basic level of 15 units in month 4. Forecasts using $w = 0.1$ reacted sluggishly, rising only to a level of 12.6 units in month 10. Forecasts using $w = 0.6$ rose rapidly to levels close to the new basic level of 15 units and then tracked the sales volume series very closely.

4.

Year	Actual Corporate Bonds Interest Rate	Next Forecast $w = 0.5$
1	4.35 = A_1	4.350 = F_2
2	4.33 = A_2	4.340 = F_3
3	4.26 = A_3	4.300 = F_4
4	4.40 = A_4	4.350 = F_5
5	4.49 = A_5	4.420 = F_6
6	5.13 = A_6	4.775 = F_7
7	5.51 = A_7	5.143 = F_8
8	6.18 = A_8	5.661 = F_9
9	7.03 = A_9	6.346 = F_{10}
10	8.04 = A_{10}	7.193 = F_{11}
11	7.39 = A_{11}	7.291 = F_{12}
12	7.21 = A_{12}	7.251 = F_{13}
13	7.44 = A_{13}	7.345 = F_{14}
14	8.57 = A_{14}	7.958 = F_{15}
15	8.83 = A_{15}	8.394 = F_{16}
16	8.43 = A_{16}	8.412 = F_{17}
17	8.02 = A_{17}	8.216 = F_{18}
18	8.73 = A_{18}	8.473 = F_{19}
19	9.63 = A_{19}	9.052 = F_{20}

The simple exponential smoothing procedure used here is appropriate for series that are relatively stable and do not have pronounced trends.

The corporate bonds interest rate series has a significant upward trend movement; therefore, the exponential smoothing forecasts generally underestimate the actual yearly values.

5.

Year	Next Forecast $w = 0.4$	Year	Next Forecast $w = 0.4$
1974	3.50 = F_2	1982	4.681578 = F_{10}
1975	3.524 = F_3	1983	4.908947 = F_{11}
1976	3.5324 = F_4	1984	4.841368 = F_{12}
1977	3.59544 = F_5	1985	4.836821 = F_{13}
1978	3.535264 = F_6	1986	4.702093 = F_{14}
1979	3.689158 = F_7	1987	5.165256 = F_{15}
1980	4.095495 = F_8	1988	5.599153 = F_{16}
1981	4.609297 = F_9	1989	6.751492 = F_{17}

The forecast of $6.751492 for 1990 is 93% of the actual $7.26 figure.

CHAPTER 12

Exercises 12.2

1. a. Weighted aggregates index, with 1983 base:

$$\frac{\Sigma P_{90}Q_{83}}{\Sigma P_{83}Q_{83}} = \frac{(\$3.35)(32) + (\$3.75)(150) + (\$4.15)(95) + (\$4.50)(12)}{(\$2.10)(32) + (\$2.50)(150) + (\$3.00)(95) + (\$3.20)(12)} \times 100$$

$$= \frac{\$1,117.95}{765.60} \times 100 = 146.02$$

   b. We cannot conclude that Sound Dynamics has a higher pricing structure in 1990 than its competitor. We know only that in 1990 Sound Dynamics tapes were priced at 146.0% of its 1983 prices, on the average, whereas in 1990, the competitor's tapes cost 130% of the 1983 prices. However, the absolute level of prices as measured by price per unit may very well be higher for Sound Dynamics' competitor. The prices of Sound Dynamics tapes have risen more, on the average, than its competitor's, but its prices per unit in 1983 may have been at a much lower level than its competitor.

2. a. For 1989 on a 1988 base:

$$\frac{\Sigma P_{89}}{\Sigma P_{88}} \cdot 100 = \frac{\$265}{\$230} \times 100 = 115.22$$

For 1990 on a 1988 base:

$$\frac{\Sigma P_{90}}{\Sigma P_{88}} \cdot 100 = \frac{\$270}{\$230} \times 100 = 117.39$$

This index is unduly influenced by high-priced stocks, which may be relatively unimportant in the consumption or purchasing pattern of the group to which the index pertains. Moreover, in some situations, the calculation of the index may be arbitrary depending on the quoted units for which the prices are stated.

   b. For 1989 on a 1988 base:

$$\frac{\Sigma P_{89}Q_{88}}{\Sigma P_{88}Q_{88}} \cdot 100 = \frac{\$52,100}{\$46,300} \times 100 = 112.53$$

For 1990 on a 1988 base:

$$\frac{\Sigma P_{90}Q_{88}}{\Sigma P_{88}Q_{88}} \cdot 100 = \frac{\$54,550}{\$46,300} \times 100 = 117.82$$

By keeping quantities fixed as of the base period, the Laspeyres index assumes a frozen consumption or purchasing pattern.

c. For 1989 on a 1988 base:

$$\frac{\Sigma P_{89}Q_{89}}{\Sigma P_{88}Q_{89}} \cdot 100 = \frac{\$66,150}{\$56,300} \times 100 = 117.50$$

For 1990 on a 1988 base:

$$\frac{\Sigma P_{90}Q_{90}}{\Sigma P_{88}Q_{90}} \cdot 100 = \frac{\$48,850}{\$39,825} \times 100 = 122.66$$

The use of current year weights makes year-to-year comparisons of price changes impossible. Another practical disadvantage is the necessity of obtaining a new set of weights each period.

Exercises 12.3

1. a. Index of car prices for 1986 on a 1990 base year:

$$\frac{\Sigma(P_{86}/P_{90})(P_{90}Q_{90})}{\Sigma(P_{90}Q_{90})}(100)$$

$$= \frac{\Sigma P_{86}Q_{90}}{\Sigma P_{90}Q_{90}}(100) = \frac{\$11,449,000}{13,500,000}(100) = 84.81$$

b. If consumers had purchased in 1986 the quantities of these three models of cars sold in 1990, then it would have cost the consumers 84.81% of the 1990 cost, or 15.19% less than the 1990 cost.

2. a. For October 11 on an October 4 base:

$$\frac{\Sigma\left(\frac{P_{11}}{P_4}\right)(P_4Q_4)}{\Sigma(P_4Q_4)}(100) = \frac{\Sigma P_{11}Q_4}{\Sigma P_4Q_4}(100)$$

$$= \frac{\$103,230}{\$99,700}(100) = 103.5$$

For October 18 on an October 4 base:

$$\frac{\Sigma\left(\frac{P_{18}}{P_4}\right)(P_4Q_4)}{\Sigma(P_4Q_4)}(100) = \frac{\Sigma P_{18}Q_4}{\Sigma P_4Q_4}(100)$$

$$= \frac{\$98,720}{\$99,700}(100) = 99.0$$

For October 25 on an October 4 base:

$$\frac{\Sigma\left(\frac{P_{25}}{P_4}\right)(P_4Q_4)}{\Sigma(P_4Q_4)}(100) = \frac{\Sigma P_{25}Q_4}{\Sigma P_4Q_4}(100)$$

$$= \frac{\$101,975}{\$99,700}(100) = 102.3$$

b. Same numerical results as in part (a).

3. a. The paradoxical results arise from the fact that an unweighted arithmetic mean of relatives offsets equal percentage increases and decreases, regardless of the bases from which the percentages were computed. For example, suppose there are only two commodities. One commodity's price increased by 10%, while that of the other decreased by 10%. The unweighted arithmetic mean of 110 and 90 would be 100, implying no change in the average level of prices. Note that the prices of these two commodities might differ greatly in order of magnitude.

b. $\frac{\Sigma P_{89}Q_{88}}{\Sigma P_{88}Q_{88}}(100) = \frac{\$285.60}{\$294.00}(100) = 97.1$

c. If the grain trader had promised the same quantities of wheat and barley for future delivery in 1989 as were promised in 1988, the cost would have been 2.9% less than in the earlier year.

Exercises 12.6

1. For 1989 on a 1988 base:

$$\frac{\Sigma Q_{89}P_{88}}{\Sigma Q_{88}P_{88}} \cdot 100 = \frac{\$451,441.49}{\$430,674.70} \times 100 = 104.8$$

For 1990 on a 1988 base:

$$\frac{\Sigma Q_{90}P_{88}}{\Sigma Q_{88}P_{88}} \cdot 100 = \frac{\$473,916.40}{\$430,674.70} \times 100 = 110.0$$

Based on the index, total feed grain production grew by 10% in 1990 on a 1988 base. This is indeed double its 4.8% growth in 1989 on a 1988 base. Therefore, the association's claim is valid.

2.

	(1)	(2)	(3)
Year	Industry Sales (in 1985 constant thousands of dollars)	Company Sales (in 1985 constant thousands of dollars)	Market Share (%) Col 2 ÷ Col 1 × 100
1989	$11,025	$2,205	20%
1990	16,667	3,666	22
1991	19,644	4,910	25

3. To convert a Washington, D.C., salary to a foreign equivalent, use the following formula:

Annual U.S. salary × (Foreign city index/100)
= Equivalent salary

Country	Equivalent Salary
Japan	$179,000
Philippines	87,000
Canada	100,000
Switzerland	187,000

4. Deflated GNP for 1987:

$$\frac{\$3,847.0 \text{ billion}}{1.177} = \$3,268.5 \text{ billion}$$

Deflated GNP for 1986:

$$\frac{\$3,721.7 \text{ billion}}{1.139} = \$3,267.5 \text{ billion}$$

"Real" GNP increased $\frac{3,268.5}{3,267.5} - 1 = 0.0\%$

5. a. City B's salary in terms of City A's dollar:

$$\$49{,}000 \times \frac{116}{90} = \$63{,}156$$

Since $63,156 is 17.0% higher than the city A salary of $54,000, the job offer in city B is preferable by a salary criterion.

Alternatively, deflating by the U.S. city cost of living index, we have:

City A: $\frac{\$54{,}000}{1.16} = \$46{,}552$

City B: $\frac{\$49{,}000}{.90} = \$54{,}494$

Again, we note that the city B figure is 17.0% higher than the city A figure.

b. Either procedure shown in the answer to part (a) is acceptable.

CHAPTER 13

Exercises 13.2

1. H_0: $p = 0.50$

   H_1: $p > 0.50$

   $\alpha = 0.01$

   $\sigma_{\bar{p}} = \sqrt{(0.50)(0.50)/185} = 0.037$

   $\bar{p} = 123/185 = 0.66$

   $z = \dfrac{(0.66 - 0.50)}{0.037} = 4.32$

   Since 4.32 > 2.33, we reject the null hypothesis of no difference in effectiveness of the two incentive programs. We conclude that the new program is better.

2. H_0: $p = 0.50$

   H_1: $p \neq 0.50$

   $\alpha = 0.05$

   $\sigma_{\bar{p}} = \sqrt{(0.50)(0.50)/382} = 0.026$

   $\bar{p} = 260/382 = 0.68$

   $z = \dfrac{(0.68 - 0.50)}{0.026} = 6.92$

   Since 6.92 > 1.96, we reject the null hypothesis that the proportion of boxes with an excess of 100 crayons is 0.50.

3. H_0: $p \leq 0.50$

   H_1: $p > 0.50$

   $\alpha = 0.05$

   $\sigma_{\bar{p}} = \sqrt{(0.50)(0.50)/32} = 0.088$

   $\bar{p} = 21/32 = 0.66$

   $z = \dfrac{(0.66 - 0.50)}{0.088} = 1.82$

   Since 1.82 > 1.65, we reject the null hypothesis that $p \leq 0.50$ and we conclude that the proportion of consumers who consider the first commercial more effective than the second exceeds 50%.

4. H_0: $p \le 0.50$

H_1: $p > 0.50$

$\alpha = 0.02$

$\sigma_{\bar{p}} = \sqrt{(0.50)(0.50)/412} = 0.025$

$\bar{p} = 252/412 = 0.61$

$$z = \frac{(0.61 - 0.50)}{0.025} = 4.4$$

Since 4.4 > 2.05, we reject the null hypothesis that $p \le 0.50$. Hence, we conclude that more than 50% of U.S. economists felt that there had been an increase in the influence of Federal Reserve stabilization policies over the past decade.

5. H_0: $p = 0.50$

H_1: $p \ne 0.50$

$\alpha = 0.01$

$$\sigma_{\bar{p}} = \sqrt{\frac{(0.50)(0.50)}{125}} = 0.04472$$

$$\bar{p} = \frac{80}{125} = 0.64$$

$$z = \frac{0.64 - 0.50}{0.04472} = 3.13$$

Since $z = 3.13 > 2.58$, we reject H_0 and conclude that there is a difference in consumer preference.

6. H_0: $p = 0.50$

H_1: $p \ne 0.50$

$\alpha = 0.05$

$$\sigma_{\bar{p}} = \sqrt{\frac{(0.50)(0.50)}{238}} = 0.0324$$

$$\bar{p} = \frac{135}{238} = 0.567$$

$$z = \frac{0.567 - 0.500}{0.0324} = 2.07$$

Since $z = 2.07 > 1.96$, we reject the hypothesis that equal proportions of students scored above and below 600.

7. H_0: $p = 0.50$

H_1: $p \ne 0.50$

$$\sigma_{\bar{p}} = \sqrt{\frac{(0.50)(0.50)}{25}} = 0.10$$

$$\bar{p} = \frac{10}{25} = 0.40$$

$$z = \frac{0.40 - 0.50}{0.10} = -1$$

Since $z = -1 > -1.96$, we reject H_0 and conclude that the respondents consider both supermarkets to be equal with respect to quality of products sold.

Exercises 13.3

1. Complete table of values

Student	X_1	X_2	$d = X_2 - X_1$	Rank of $\lvert d \rvert$	Signed Rank Rank (+)	Signed Rank Rank (−)
A	550	560	+10	1.5	1.5	
B	490	530	+40	6.5	6.5	
C	610	580	−30	5		5
D	570	650	+80	11	11	
E	670	660	−10	1.5	1.5	1.5
F	480	500	+20	3.5	3.5	
G	720	680	−40	6.5		6.5
H	630	570	−60	9		9
I	500	570	+70	10	10	
J	660	710	+50	8	8	
K	540	520	−20	3.5		3.5
L	570	570	0			
					40.5	25.5 = T

$n = 11$ $T = 25.5$ $T_{0.05} = 13$.
Since $T = 25.5 > T_{0.05} = 13$, we retain the null hypothesis of identical population distributions. Therefore, we cannot conclude that the scores on the second test are significantly higher than the scores on the first test.

2. Complete table of values

Sales Representative	X_1	X_2	$d = X_2 - X_1$	Rank of $\lvert d \rvert$	Signed Rank Rank (+)	Signed Rank Rank (−)
A	22	25	+3	4	4	
B	10	14	+4	5	5	
C	15	17	+2	3	3	
D	21	31	+10	9	9	
E	28	33	+5	6	6	
F	27	27	0			
G	33	32	−1	1.5		1.5
H	18	19	+1	1.5	1.5	
I	17	28	+11	10	10	
J	16	22	+6	7	7	
K	15	22	+7	8	8	
					53.5	1.5 = T

$n = 10$ $T = 1.5$ $T_{0.01} = 5$.
Since $T = 1.5 < T_{0.01} = 5$, we reject the null hypothesis of identical population distributions. Therefore, we conclude that the promotional campaign was accompanied by an increase in number of sales.

3.

Complete table of values

City	X_1	X_2	$d = X_2 - X_1$	Rank of $\lvert d \rvert$	Signed Rank: Rank (+)	Signed Rank: Rank (-)
Atlanta	110	42	-68	5		5
Boston	122	70	-52	2		2
Chicago	467	301	-166	9		9
Detroit	206	325	+119	7	7	
Los Angeles	340	283	-57	3		3
Miami	76	38	-38	1		1
New Orleans	134	75	-59	4		4
New York	643	397	-246	10		10
Philadelphia	389	227	-162	8		8
San Francisco	291	183	-108	6		6
					T = 7	48

4. $\mu_T = 55(55 + 1)/4 = 770$

   $\sigma_T = \sqrt{55(55+1)(110+1)/24} = 119.35$

   $z = (510 - 770)/119.35 = -2.18$

   Since $-2.18 < -1.96$, we reject the null hypothesis of identical population distributions.

Exercises 13.4

In the solutions to section 13.4, the data are ranked from highest to lowest, with rank 1 assigned to the highest value.

1. $R_1 = 112$, $R_2 = 141$, $n_1 = 11$, $n_2 = 11$, $U = 75$, $\mu_U = 60.5$

   $$\sigma_U = \sqrt{\frac{(11)(11)(11+11+1)}{12}} = 15.23$$

   $z = (75 - 60.5)/15.23 = 0.95$

   Since $0.95 < 2.58$, we retain the hypothesis that the groups were drawn from populations having the same average job performance.

2. $R_1 = 110$, $R_2 = 190$, $n_1 = 12$, $n_2 = 12$, $U = 112$, $\mu_U = 72$, $\alpha = 0.05$

   $\sigma_U = \sqrt{(12)(12)(25)/12} = 17.32$

   $z = (112 - 72)/17.32 = 2.31$

   Since $2.31 > 1.96$, we reject the hypothesis of no difference between the average research and development expenditure levels of the two industries.

3. $R_1 = 146$, $R_2 = 260$, $n_1 = 14$, $n_2 = 14$, $U = 155$, $\mu_U = 98$, $\alpha = 0.01$

   $\sigma_U = \sqrt{(14)(14)(29)/12} = 21.76$

   $z = (155 - 98)/21.76 = 2.62$

   Since $2.62 > 2.58$, we reject the hypothesis of no difference between the average sales levels for the two samples.

4. $R_1 = 143$, $R_2 = 263$, $n_1 = 13$, $n_2 = 15$, $U = 143$, $\mu_U = 97.5$, $\alpha = 0.05$

$\sigma_U = \sqrt{(13)(15)(29)/12} = 21.7$

$z = (143 - 97.5)/21.7 = 2.10$

Since 2.10 > 1.96, we reject the hypothesis of no difference between the true average times for the two different methods.

5. $R_1 = 198$, $R_2 = 208$, $n_1 = 14$, $n_2 = 14$, $U = 103$, $\mu_U = 98$

$\sigma_U = \sqrt{(14)(14)(29)/12} = 21.8$

$z = (103 - 98)/21.8 = 0.23$

Since 0.23 < 2.58, we retain the hypothesis that the samples were drawn from populations having the same average profit.

6. $R_1 = 168$, $R_2 = 238$, $n_1 = 13$, $n_2 = 15$, $U = 118$, $\mu_U = 97.5$, $\alpha = 0.05$

$\sigma_U = \sqrt{(13)(15)(29)/12} = 21.7$

$z = (118 - 97.5)/21.7 = 0.94$

Since 0.94 < 1.96, we retain the hypothesis of no difference between the true average times for the two different methods.

Exercises 13.5

1. $n_1 = 22$, $n_2 = 28$, $r = 26$

$$\mu_r = \frac{2(22)(28)}{22+28} + 1 = 25.64$$

$$\sigma_r = \sqrt{\frac{2(22)(28)[(2)(22)(28) - 22 - 28]}{(22+28)^2(22+28-1)}} = 3.45$$

$z = (26 - 25.64)/3.45 = 0.10$

Since $|0.10| < 1.96$ and $|0.10| < 2.58$, we retain the hypothesis of randomness of runs of even and odd digits at the 0.05 and 0.01 levels of significance.

2. $n_1 = 24$, $n_2 = 26$, $r = 20$

$$\mu_r = \frac{2(24)(26)}{24+26} + 1 = 25.96$$

$$\sigma_r = \sqrt{\frac{2(24)(26)[(2)(24)(26) - 24 - 26]}{(24+26)^2(24+26-1)}} = 3.49$$

$$z = \frac{20 - 25.96}{3.49} = -1.71$$

Since $|-1.71| < 1.96$ and $|-1.71| < 2.58$, we retain the hypothesis of randomness of runs above and below the mean 4.5 at both the 0.05 and 0.01 levels of significance.

3. $n_1 = 10$, $n_2 = 10$, $r = 4$

$$\mu_r = \frac{2(10)(10)}{10+10} + 1 = 11$$

$$\sigma_r = \sqrt{\frac{2(10)(10)[2(10)(10) - 10 - 10]}{(10+10)^2(10+10-1)}} = 2.18$$

$z = (4 - 11)/2.18 = -3.21$

Since $|-3.21| > 2.58$, we reject the hypothesis of randomness of runs above and below the median. Since runs below the median tend to occur in the early part of the series, and runs above the median in the later part, there is evidence of an increasing trend in the weekly unemployment percentages.

4. $n_1 = 15, \quad n_2 = 11, \quad r = 16$

$$\mu_r = \frac{2(15)(11)}{15 + 11} + 1 = 13.69$$

$$\sigma_r = \sqrt{\frac{[2(15)(11)][(2)(15)(11) - 15 - 11]}{(15+11)^2(15 + 11 - 1)}} = 2.44$$

$$z = \frac{16 - 13.69}{2.44} = 0.95$$

Since $0.95 < 1.96$, we retain the null hypothesis of randomness of runs above and below the mean.

5. $n_1 = 21, \quad n_2 = 19, \quad r = 15$

$$\mu_r = \frac{(2)(21)(19)}{21 + 19} + 1 = 20.95$$

$$\sigma_r = \sqrt{\frac{(2)(21)(19)[2(21)(19) - 21 - 19]}{(21+19)^2(21 + 19 - 1)}} = 3.11$$

$$z = \frac{15 - 20.95}{3.11} = -1.91$$

Since $-1.91 > -2.58$, we retain the hypothesis of randomness of runs above and below the specified weight, at the 0.01 level of significance.

Exercises 13.6

1.

Amount of policy:	18	28	34	49	54	56	57	57	68	74	87	96	105	111	115	118	122	125	134	145	174	190	198	205	206
Rank:	1	2	3	4	5	6	7	8	9	10	11	12	13	14	15	16	17	18	19	20	21	22	23	24	25

$\nu = 4 - 1 = 3$

$\chi^2_{0.01} = 11.345$

$$K = \frac{12}{25(25+1)}\left(\frac{74^2}{7} + \frac{76^2}{6} + \frac{95^2}{6} + \frac{80^2}{6}\right) - 3(25+1) = 1.676$$

Since $K = 1.676 < 11.345$, we cannot reject the hypothesis of identically distributed populations.

2. a.

Number of accounts collected:	20	25	26	30	31	32	35	36	38	39	40	42	45	46	48	49	50	52
Rank:	1	2	3	4	5	6	7	8	9	10	11	12	13	14	15	16	17	18

$\nu = 3 - 1 = 2$

$\chi^2_{0.01} = 9.210$

$$K = \frac{12}{18(18+1)}\left(\frac{36^2}{6} + \frac{62^2}{6} + \frac{73^2}{6}\right) - 3(19) = 4.222$$

Since $4.222 < 9.210$, we cannot reject the null hypothesis of no difference in effectiveness among the three collectors at the 1% level of significance.

b. Analysis of variance table

(1) Source of Variation	(2) Sum of Squares	(3) Degrees of Freedom	(4) Mean Squares
Between collectors	366.33	2	183.17
Error	1,127.67	15	75.18
	1,494.00	17	

$F_{0.01}(2,\ 15) = 6.36$

Since 2.44 < 6.36, we cannot reject the null hypothesis of no difference in average numbers of accounts removed from delinquency by the three collectors.

3. Number of defectives: 0 2 3 4 6 7 8 10 12 13 14 15 16 17 18 19 20 21 22 23 24 25 27 28 29 30 31
Rank: 1 2 3 4 5 6 7 8 9 10 11 12 13 14 15 16 17 18 19 20 21 22 23 24 25 26 27

$\nu = 4 - 1 = 3$

$\chi^2_{0.01} = 11.345$

$$K = \frac{12}{27(27+1)}\left(\frac{29^2}{6} + \frac{162^2}{8} + \frac{87^2}{7} + \frac{100^2}{6}\right) - 3(27+1) = 13.915$$

Since $K = 13.915 > 11.345$, we reject the hypothesis of identically distributed populations.

4. a. Number of units sold: 30 36 38 43 47 52 55 59 61 64 66 67 69 73 75 77 80 82
Rank: 1 2 3 4 5 6 7 8 9 10 11 12 13 14 15 16 17 18

$\nu = 3 - 1 = 2;\ \chi^2_{0.01} = 9.210$

$$K = \frac{12}{18(18+1)}\left(\frac{31^2}{6} + \frac{68^2}{6} + \frac{72^2}{6}\right) - 3(18+1) = 5.977$$

Since 5.977 < 9.210, we cannot reject the null hypothesis of no difference in effectiveness among the three advertisement designs at the 1% level of significance.

b. Analysis of variance table

(1) Source of Variation	(2) Sum of Squares	(3) Degrees of Freedom	(4) Mean Squares
Between columns	1425	2	712.50
Between rows	2831	15	188.73
Total	4256	17	

$$F(2,\ 15) = \frac{712.50}{188.73} = 3.78$$

$F_{0.01}(2,\ 15) = 6.36$

Since 3.78 < 6.36, we cannot reject the null hypothesis of no difference in average numbers of sales resulting from the three advertisements.

Exercises 13.7

1. $r_r = 1 - \dfrac{6(18)}{12(144-1)} = 0.94$

2. $r_r = 1 - \dfrac{6(116)}{10(100-1)} = 0.30$

3. $r_r = 1 - \dfrac{6(44)}{10(10^2-1)} = 0.733$

4. $r_r = 1 - \dfrac{6(62)}{12(12^2-1)} = 0.78$

   $t = \dfrac{0.78}{\sqrt{(1-0.61)/(12-2)}} = 3.95$

   Since 3.95 > 2.228 (two-tailed test), we reject the null hypothesis of no rank correlation.

CHAPTER 14

Exercises 14.4

1. The sum of the prior probabilities is not equal to one.

2. *P*(wooden racket) = 0.50
   P(metal racket) = 0.375
   P(fiberglass racket) = 0.215

3. Gain from cost reduction = 1% of $2,000,000 = $20,000
   Expected gain(campaign) = (0.8)(0.13)(0.11)($2,000,000)
   = $22,880
   The better act is the advertising campaign.

4. Expected profit(playing game) = (1/13)($10,000) + (12/13)(-$800)
   = $30.77
   Therefore, on an expected monetary value basis, it pays to play the game.

5. Money figures are in tens of thousands of dollars.
   Expected profit(1) = 0.1(2) + 0.2(4) + 0.3(5) + 0.2(6) + 0.2(7) = 5.1
   Expected profit(2) = 0.1(0) + 0.2(5) + 0.3(6) + 0.2(7) + 0.2(7) = 5.6
   Expected profit(3) = 0.1(-1) + 0.2(0) + 0.3(5) + 0.2(6) + 0.2(7) = 4.0
   Expected profit(4) = 0.1(-1) + 0.2(-1) + 0.3(0) + 0.2(6) + 0.2(6) = 2.1
   Expected profit(5) = 0.1(-1) + 0.2(-1) + 0.3(-1) + 0.2(0) + 0.2(6) = 0.6
   Therefore, Dealer A should set her price at price 2, and her expected profit will be $56,000.

6. The cost per year is $4,900. The expected gain from the information is (0.05)($80,000) = $4,000. Since cost exceeds the expected gain, do not include newsletters.

7. Expected profit(calculator) = 0.50(0.10) + 0.50(0.02)
   = 6%
   Therefore, the firm should not manufacture the calculator and should instead invest in risk-free securities at the rate of 8%.

8. 0.12(x) + (-0.03)(1.00 - x) = 0
   x = 20%
   Therefore, when the chance of the bill passing is 20%, the candidate will be statistically indifferent.

9. Expected profit(high) = 0.70)(10) + 0.30(-15) = 2.5
   Expected profit(average) = 0.70(4) + 0.30(-2) = 2.2
   Expected profit(low) = 0.70(2) + 0.30(1) = 1.7
   She would choose the high-risk portfolio if she wanted to maximize expected profit.
   EOL(high) = 0(0.70) + 16(0.30) = 4.8
   EOL(average) = 6(0.70) + 3(0.30) = 5.1
   EOL(low) = 8(0.70) + 0(0.30) = 5.6
   She would again choose the high-risk portfolio if she wanted to minimize expected opportunity loss.

10 a.

Opportunity loss table

State of Nature	Advertising Costs High	Average	Low
Severe recession	10	6	0
Mild recession	6	2	0
Weak recovery	0	1	2
Strong recovery	0	3	8

b. EOL(high) = 10(0.20) + 6(0.25) + 0(0.55) = 3.5
EOL(average) = 6(0.20) + 2(0.25) + 1(0.40) + 3(0.15)
= 2.55
EOL(low) = 0(0.20) + 0(0.25) + 2(0.40) + 8(0.15)
= 2.00

The manufacturer should choose the low advertising cost budget if the company wishes to minimize the expected opportunity loss.

11.

Type	Probability
Nonfiction	0.06
Classical fiction	0.30
Modern fiction	0.53
Sports	0.11

12. Return from 14% commercial paper: $63,000

[*P*(good business condition)($112,500)]
+ [1 − *P*(good business condition)]
· ($36,000) = $63,000

P(good business condition) = 0.353

13. Expected profit—unmodified = $20
Expected profit—modified = [(0.3)(35)]
+ [(0.5)(23)]
+ [(0.2)(15)]
= $25

Decision: Go for modification.

14.

Profit table

Number Demanded	Probability	Number of Television Sets in Stock 0	1	2	3	4	5
0	0.10	0	-100	-200	-300	-400	-500
1	0.10	0	250	150	50	-50	-150
2	0.15	0	250	500	400	300	200
3	0.35	0	250	500	750	650	550
4	0.20	0	250	500	750	1,000	900
5	0.10	0	250	500	750	1,000	1,250
Expected values ($)		0	215	395	522.50	527.50	462.50

The optimal stock level is 4 television sets.
The expected profit is $527.50.

Exercises 14.6

1. See section 14.5.
2. The expected value of perfect information is the expected opportunity loss of the optimal act under uncertainty.
3. No, because the opportunity loss table gives for each state of nature only the difference between payoffs for different acts. To compute payoffs, we need to know the actual payoff for at least one act for each state of nature.
4. Opportunity loss table

Demand	Work	Do Not Work
Good	$0	$100
Fair	0	50
Poor	0	0

5. (1) In units of $10,000,

   $EOL(A_1)$ = (0.2)(150) + (0.4)(25) + (0.3)(5) + (0.1)(10) = 42.5
   $EOL(A_2)$ = (0.2)(130) + (0.4)(20) + (0.3)(15) + (0.1)(15) = 40.0
   $EOL(A_3)$ = (0.2)(50) + (0.4)(0) + (0.3)(10) + (0.1)(0) = 13.0
   $EOL(A_4)$ = (0.2)(0) + (0.4)(10) + (0.3)(0) + (0.1)(5) = 4.5
   Therefore, EVPI = minimum EOL = 4.5

   (2) Under certainty, the expected payoff is
   (0.2)(250) + (0.4)(110) + (0.3)(75) + (0.1)(70) = 123.5
   Under uncertainty, the expected payoff of the best act, A_4, is
   (0.2)(250) + (0.4)(100) + (0.3)(75) + (0.1)(65) = 119.0
   EVPI = 123.5 - 119.0 = 4.5

6. Money figures are in units of $1,000.

   a. Expected profit with perfect information
   = (0.5)(20) + (0.3)(14) + (0.2)(10) = 16.2

   b. Expected profits:
   A_1 = (0.5)(20) + (0.3)(10) + (0.2)(4) = 13.8
   A_2 = (0.5)(17) + (0.3)(14) + (0.2)(7) = 14.1
   A_3 = (0.5)(18) + (0.3)(14) + (0.2)(5) = 14.2
   A_4 = (0.5)(13) + (0.3)(12) + (0.2)(10) = 12.1
   The optimal act is A_3. Hence, the expected profit under uncertainty is 14.2.

   c. EVPI = 16.2 - 14.2 = 2.0

7. Opportunity loss table

	A_1	A_2
Outcome	High	Do Not Invest
Success	0	$60,000
Failure	$30,000	0

$EOL(A_1)$ = 2/3(0) + 1/3($30,000) = $10,000
$EOL(A_2)$ = 2/3($60,000) + 1/3(0) = $40,000
EVPI = $10,000

Frey should invest in the company.

8. Under certainty:

   Expected return = (0.60)(0) + (0.40)($3,500)
   = $1,400

   Under uncertainty:

   Expected return (take deductions)
   = (0.60)(-$2,000) + (0.40)(+$3,500) = $200

   Expected return(do not take deductions)
   = (0.60)(0) + (0.40)(0) = 0

   EVPI = $1,400 - $200 = $1,200

   Alternatively,

   EOL(take deductions) = (0.60)($2,000) + (0.40)(0)
   = $1,200

   EOL(do not take deductions)
   = (0.60)(0) + (0.40)($3,500) = $1,400

   EVPI = $1,200

9. a. Expected profit with perfect information
   = (0.20)($6,000) + (0.80)($20,000) = $17,200

   b. Expected profit($1,800)
   = (0.20)($6,000) + (0.80)($18,000) = $15,600

   Expected profit($2,000)
   = (0.2)($4,000) + (0.8)($20,000) = $16,800

   The optimal price is $2,000. The expected profit under uncertainty is $16,800.

   c. EVPI = $17,200 - $16,800 = $400. Jasper should be willing to pay no more than $400 for the information.

10. a. Expected gain(buy) = (0.3)($20,000) + (0.3)($10,000) + (0.4)(-$2,000)
    = $8,200

    Since the expected gain is positive, you should buy the computer.

    b. Expected gain with perfect information
    = (0.3)($20,000) + (0.3)($10,000) + (0.4)($0) = $9,000

    Therefore, EVPI = $9,000 - $8,200 = $800

11. EOL(work) = (0.3)($0) + (0.4)($0) + (0.3)($0) = $0

    EOL(don't work) = (0.3)($100) + (0.4)($50) + (0.3)($0)
    = $50

    The cab driver's optimal decision is to work.

12. a. In $10,000 units,

    EOL(A_1) = (0.4)(2) + (0.3)(0) + (0.2)(3) + (0.1)(3)
    = 1.7

    EOL(A_2) = (0.4)(2) + (0.3)(1) + (0.2)(0) + (0.1)(2)
    = 1.3

    EOL(A_3) = (0.4)(3) + (0.3)(2) + (0.2)(1) + (0.1)(0)
    = 2.0

    EOL(A_4) = (0.4)(0) + (0.3)(4) + (0.2)(3) + (0.1)(3)
    = 2.1

    b. EVPI = 1.3

    c. Since A_2 has the lowest EOL, the optimal decision is A_2.

Exercises 14.8

1. a. Disagree. Although the expected monetary return of purchasing life insurance may be negative, the expected utility will tend to be positive because of the shape of most individuals' utility functions.

b. The premium cost for automobile insurance exceeds the company's expected losses. If a company has abundant assets, it will be rational for the firm to make decisions based on expected monetary value for alternatives involving only a small percentage of total assets. On the other hand, a single loss of a few thousand dollars may be relatively catastrophic for an individual, leading to a risk avoider's utility function for the individual.

2. a. Expected utility(buy the stock)
= (0.4)(45) + (0.6)(-15) = 9 units of utility

b. Expected utility(buy government securities)
= 10 units of utility
Therefore, you should buy the government securities.

3. a. Expected monetary loss(dispute)
= (0.95)($550) + (0.05)($50) = $525
Since $525 > $500, do not dispute.

b. Expected utility(don't dispute) = -425 units of utility
Expected utility(dispute) = (0.95)(-440) + (0.05)(-4)
= -418.2 units of utility
Therefore, the best act is to dispute the bill.

4. a. Expected gain(100% interest)
= (0.8)(-$1) + (0.1)($3) + (0.1)($8) = $0.3 million
Expected gain(50% interest)
= (0.8)(-$0.5) + (0.1)($1.5) + (0.1)($4) = $0.15 million
Expected gain(don't drill) = 0
The best act is to drill with a 100% interest.

b. Expected utility(100% interest)
= (0.8)(-30) + (0.1)(90) + (0.1)(240) = 9 units of utility
Expected utility(50% interest)
= (0.8)(-15) + (0.1)(45) + (0.1)(120) = 4.5 units of utility
The best act is to drill with a 100% interest.

c. The fact that the decision using an expected utility criterion is the same as that using an expected monetary value criterion is no basis to make conclusions on risk aversion. However, in Drillwell's utility function, note that the utility figures are always 30 times the monetary figures, that is, monetary values and utilities are linearly related. Hence, we conclude that Drillwell's management is *risk neutral*.

5. a. See figure (p. 126). The utility function appears to be that of a risk avoider until a figure between $50,000 and $75,000. From then on, the curve describes a risk preferrer.

b. $E[U(\text{buy})] = (0.5)(-40) + (0.2)(6) + (0.1)(10) + (0.2)(40) = -9.8$
Therefore, the investor should not buy the franchise.

c. $E[U(1/4)] = (0.5)(-2) + (0.2)(1.2) + (0.1)(2.5) + (0.2)(6.2) = 0.73$
$E[U(1/2)] = (0.5)(-4.2) + (0.2)(2.5) + (0.1)(6.0) + (0.2)(12.5) = 1.5$
$E[U(3/4)] = (0.5)(-10) + (0.2)(5.8) + (0.1)(7.5) + (0.2)(26) = 2.11$
Therefore, the best act is to buy a three-fourths interest.

6. a. Expected monetary return
= (0.5)($200,000) + (0.5)(-$100,000) = $50,000
He would be willing to pay at most $50,000.

b. Expected utility of final wealth
$= (0.5)(\sqrt{300,000}) + (0.5)(\sqrt{0}) = 273.9$ units of utility
$U(\$100,000) = \sqrt{100,000} = 316.2$

Since 316.2 > 273.9, the individual will not pay anything to invest.

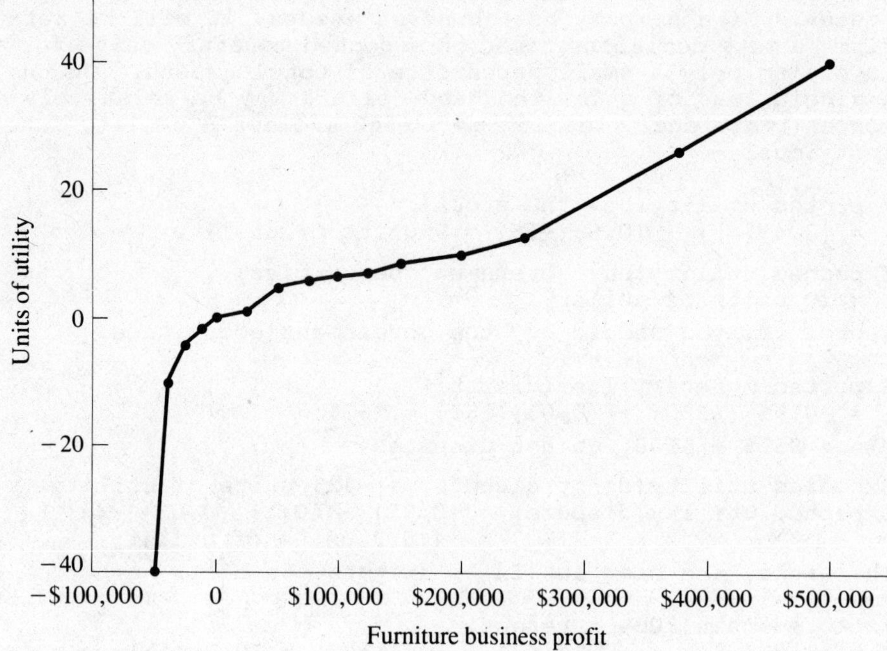
40
20
0
−20
−40
Units of utility
−$100,000
0
$100,000
$200,000
$300,000
$400,000
$500,000
Furniture business profit

CHAPTER 15

Exercises 15.2

1.

State of Nature	$P_0(\theta)$	$P(X\|\theta)$	$P_0(\theta)P(X\|\theta)$	$P_1(\theta\|X)$
θ_1	0.8	0.4	0.32	0.73
θ_2	0.2	0.6	0.12	0.27
			0.44	1.00

2.

State of Nature	$P_0(\theta)$	$P(X\|\theta)$	$P_0(\theta)P(X\|\theta)$	$P_1(\theta\|X)$
θ_1	0.10	0.20	0.020	0.037
θ_2	0.20	0.10	0.020	0.037
θ_3	0.30	0.50	0.150	0.280
θ_4	0.25	0.90	0.225	0.421
θ_5	0.15	0.80	0.120	0.224
			0.535	1.000

3.

State of Nature	$P_0(\theta)$	$P(X\|\theta)$	$P_0(\theta)P(X\|\theta)$	$P_1(\theta\|X)$
θ_1	0.2	0.05	0.01	0.031
θ_2	0.6	0.20	0.12	0.375
θ_3	0.2	0.95	0.19	0.594
			0.32	1.000

4. No, because after sampling the best act remains the same. The actual value of the sample information is zero.

5.

State of Nature	$P_0(\theta)$	$P(X\|\theta)$	$P_0(\theta)P(X\|\theta)$	$P_1(\theta\|X)$
θ_1	x	0.5	$0.5x$	$x = 0.25$
θ_2	$1 - x$	0.5	$0.5(1 - x)$	$(1 - x) = 0.75$
			0.5	1.00

Therefore, the prior probabilities are $P_0(\theta_1) = 0.25$ and $P_0(\theta_2) = 0.75$.

6. No. Although both prior and sample information indicate that θ_2 is true, the relative sizes of payoffs determine whether act A_2 is better than A_1. The expected payoff of act A_1 can conceivably exceed that of act A_2.

7.

State of Nature	$P_0(\theta)$	$P(X\|\theta)$	$P_0(\theta)P(X\|\theta)$	$P_1(\theta\|X)$
θ_1	0.5	0.55	0.275	0.846
θ_2	0.5	0.10	0.050	0.154
			0.325	1.000

Posterior expected profit = ($5)(0.846)
+ (-$2)(0.154) million
= $3.922 million

8. Prior expected profit = (-$15,000)(0.20)
+ (-$5,000)(0.35)
+ ($28,000)(0.45)
= $7,850

Before considering the additional information, her best action is to wait six months.

State of Nature	$P_0(\theta)$	$P(X\|\theta)$	$P_0(\theta)P(X\|\theta)$	$P_1(\theta\|X)$
θ_1: Higher interest rates	0.20	0.10	0.02	0.044
θ_2: No change	0.35	0.20	0.07	0.156
θ_3: Lower interest rates	0.45	0.80	0.36	0.800
			0.45	1.000

Posterior expected profit = (-$15,000)(0.044)
+ (-$5,000)(0.156)
+ ($28,000)(0.800)
= $20,960

After considering the additional information, her best action is still to wait six months.

9.

State of Nature	$P_0(\theta)$	$P(X\|\theta)$	$P_0(\theta)P(X\|\theta)$	$P_1(\theta\|X)$
θ_1	0.4	0.9	0.36	0.75
θ_2	0.6	0.2	0.12	0.25
			0.48	1.00

Posterior expected payoff for act A_1 = (0.75)(10)
+ (0.25)(100)
= 32.5

Posterior expected payoff for act A_2 = (0.75)(30)
+ (0.25)(20)
= 27.5

After considering the additional information, A_1 is the better course of action.

Posterior expected payoff with perfect information
= (0.75)(30) + (0.25)(100)
= $47.5 thousand

Therefore, posterior EVPI = $47.5 - $32.5 = $15 thousand

Exercises 15.3

1. a.

p	$P_0(p)$	$P(X = 1 \mid n = 20, p)$	Joint Probability	$P_1(p)$
0.10	0.80	0.2701	0.21608	0.95
0.20	0.20	0.0577	0.01154	0.05
			0.22762	1.00

b. $P_1(0.10) = 0.89$ $\quad$ $P_1(0.20) = 0.11$

c. $P_1(0.10) = 0.79$ $\quad$ $P_1(0.20) = 0.21$

2.

μ	$P_0(p)$	$P(X = 7 \mid \mu)$	$P_0(\mu)P(X = 7 \mid \mu)$	$P_1(\mu)$
6	0.7	0.138	0.0966	0.68
7	0.3	0.149	0.0447	0.32
			0.1413	1.00

3. a. EOL(accept) = (0.4)($0) + (0.2)($250) + (0.2)($500) + (0.2)($750) = $300

b.

$P(X = 2 \mid p)$	$P_1(p)$
0.1887	0.37
0.2852	0.28
0.2293	0.22
0.1369	0.13

EOL(accept) = (0.37)($0) + (0.28)($250) + (0.22)($500) + (0.13)($750) = $277.50

4. a. $P(0.05 \mid 1) = 0.45$ $\quad$ $P(0.10 \mid 1) = 0.42$
$P(0.15 \mid 1) = 0.11$ $\quad$ $P(0.20 \mid 1) = 0.02$

b. $P(0.05 \mid 3) = 0.11$ $\quad$ $P(0.10 \mid 3) = 0.47$
$P(0.15 \mid 3) = 0.30$ $\quad$ $P(0.20 \mid 3) = 0.12$

5. a. Benefit(Dodd) = (780,000)($15) − (20,000)($60) + (1 − x)(20,000)($15) = $10,800,000 − $300,000$x$

Benefit(Todd) = (1,120,000)($15) − (80,000)($60) + (1 − x)(80,000)($15) = $13,200,000 − $1,200,000$x$

b. For Dodd County:

$$E_0(\theta) = (0.4)(0.05) + (0.3)(0.10) + (0.3)(0.15) + (0.0)(0.20) = 0.095$$

For Todd County:

$$E_0(\theta) = (0.0)(0.05) + (0.2)(0.10) + (0.6)(0.15) + (0.2)(0.20) = 0.15$$

E_0(benefit to Dodd) = \$10,800,000 - (\$300,000)(0.095)
= \$10,771,500

E_0(benefit to Todd) = \$13,200,000 - (\$1,200,000)(0.15)
= \$13,020,000

According to this comparison, building the reservoir in Todd County is preferable.

c. Dodd County

θ	$P_0(\theta)$	$P(X = 4 \mid p = \theta,\ n = 20)$	Joint Probability	$P_1(\theta)$
0.05	0.4	0.0133	0.00532	0.061
0.10	0.3	0.0898	0.02694	0.310
0.15	0.3	0.1821	0.05463	0.629
			0.08689	1.000

$E_1(\theta)$ = (0.061)(0.05) + (0.310)(0.10) + (0.629)(0.15)
= 0.13

E_1(benefit to Dodd) = \$10,800,000 - (\$300,000)(0.13)
= \$10,761,000

Todd County

θ	$P_0(\theta)$	$P(X = 6 \mid p = \theta,\ n = 20)$	Joint Probability	$P_1(\theta)$
0.10	0.2	0.0089	0.00178	0.035
0.15	0.6	0.0454	0.02724	0.536
0.20	0.2	0.1091	0.02182	0.429
			0.05084	1.000

$E_1(\theta)$ = (0.035)(0.10) + (0.536)(0.15) + (0.429)(0.20)
= 0.17

E_1(benefit to Todd) = \$13,200,000 - (\$1,200,000)(0.17)
= \$12,996,000

Therefore, the comparison of expected net benefits indicates that building the reservoir in Todd County is still preferable.

6. a. Complete table of values

Event p	Prior Probability $P_0(p)$	Conditional Probability $P(X = 4 \mid n = 20, p)$	Joint Probability $P_0(p)P(X = 4 \mid n = 20, p)$	Posterior Probability $P_1(p)$
0.10	0.20	0.0898	0.01796	0.1174
0.20	0.35	0.2182	0.07637	0.4991
0.30	0.45	0.1304	0.05868	0.3835
			0.15301	1.0000

b. Complete table of values

Event p	Joint Probability $P_0(p)$	Conditional Probability $P(X = 20 \mid n = 100, p)$	Joint Probability $P_0(p)P(X = 20 \mid n = 100, p)$	Posterior Probability $P_1(p)$
0.10	0.20	0.0012	0.00024	0.00625
0.20	0.35	0.0993	0.03476	0.90474
0.30	0.45	0.0076	0.00342	0.08901
			0.03842	1.00000

7. Prior mean = (0.10)(0.20) + (0.20)(0.35) + (0.30)(0.45)
= 0.225

For part (a), posterior mean = (0.10)(0.1174) + (0.20)(0.4991)
+ (0.30)(0.3835)
= 0.2266

For part (b), posterior mean = (0.10)(0.00625) + (0.20)(0.90474)
+ (0.30)(0.08901)
= 0.2083

CHAPTER 16

Exercises 16.2

1. See pages 760-61.

2.

State of Nature	$P(\theta)$	$P(X\|\theta)$	$P(Y\|\theta)$	$P(\theta)P(X\|\theta)$	$P(\theta)P(Y\|\theta)$	$P(\theta\|X)$	$P(\theta\|Y)$
θ_1	0.3	0.6	0.4	0.18	0.12	0.46	0.20
θ_2	0.7	0.3	0.7	0.21	0.49	0.54	0.80
				0.39	0.61	1.00	1.00

3. Let X_1 = Forecast that oil will be found
   X_2 = Forecast that oil will not be found

   $P(\theta_1|X_1) = 0.786$ $\quad$ $P(\theta_2|X_1) = 0.214$

   $P(\theta_1|X_2) = 0.288$ $\quad$ $P(\theta_2|X_2) = 0.712$

4. a. and b. See figure.

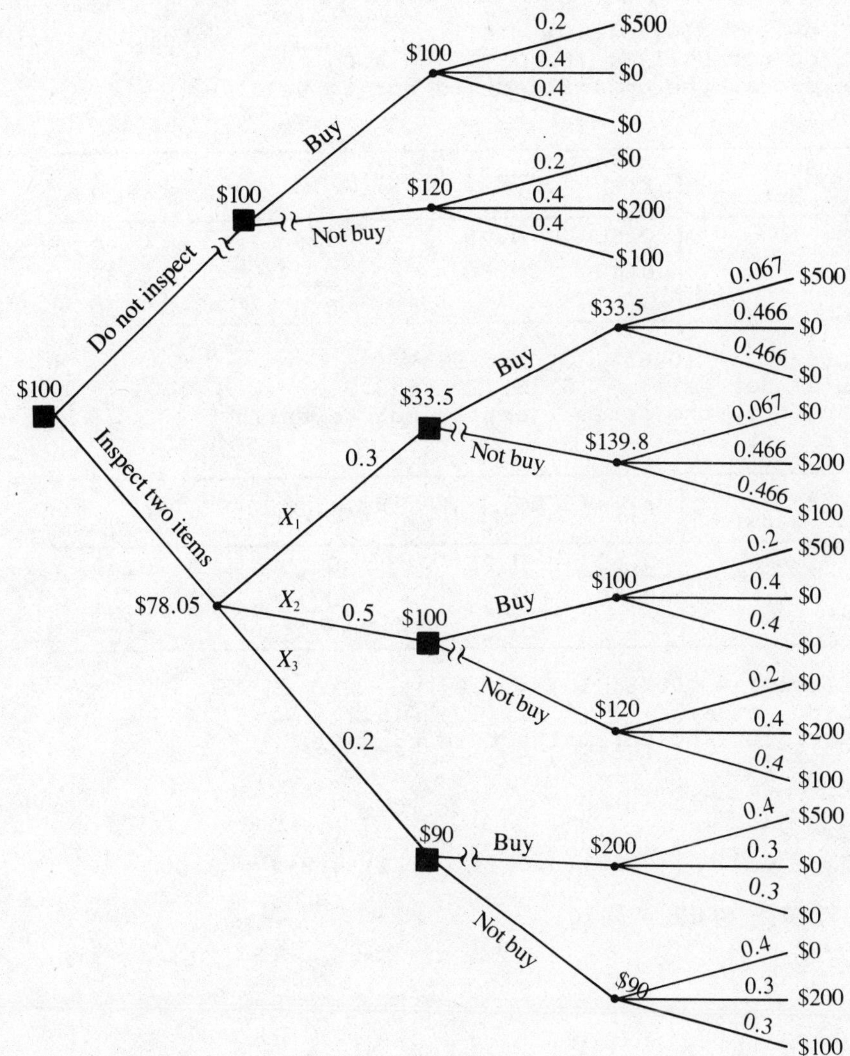

c. EVPI(before) = $100

d. EVSI = $100 - $78.05 = $21.95

5. a. (1) EOL(build) = (0.5)(12) = 6.0
EOL(do not build) = (0.5)(17) = 8.5
Therefore, the optimal act is to build.

(2) $P(\theta|X_1)$ = 0.571; $P(\theta|X_1)$ = 0.429
EOL(build) = (0.429)(12) = 5.148
EOL(do not build) = (0.571)(17) = 9.707
Therefore, the optimal act is still to build.

(3) $P(\theta_1|X_2)$ = 0.421; $P(\theta_2|X_2)$ = 0.579
EOL(build) = (0.579)(12) = 6.948
EOL(do not build) = (0.421)(17) = 7.157
Therefore, the optimal act is still to build.

(4) $P(X_1)$ = 0.525
$P(X_2)$ = 0.475

(5) EVSI = 6 - [(0.525)(5.148) + (0.475)(6.948)] = 0

b. No, because neither X_1 nor X_2 changes the optimal act. The answer is also no because EVSI = 0.

6. In this exercise, money figures are units of $10,000.

a. (1) EOL(sell) = (0.60)(10) = 6.0
EOL(do not sell) = (0.40)(10) = 4.0
Therefore, the optimal act is not to sell.

(2)

State of Nature	$P(\theta)$	$P(X_1\|\theta)$	$P(\theta)P(X_1\|\theta)$	$P(\theta\|X_1)$
θ_1	0.60	0.75	0.45	0.65
θ_2	0.40	0.60	0.24	0.35
			0.69	1.00

EOL(sell) = (0.65)(10) = 6.5
EOL(do not sell) = (0.35)(10) = 3.5
Therefore, the optimal act is not to sell.

(3)

State of Nature	$P(\theta)$	$P(X_2\|\theta)$	$P(\theta)P(X_2\|\theta)$	$P(\theta\|X_2)$
θ_1	0.60	0.25	0.15	0.48
θ_2	0.40	0.40	0.16	0.52
			0.31	1.00

EOL(sell) = (0.48)(10) = 4.8
EOL(do not sell) = (0.52)(10) = 5.2
Therefore, the optimal act is to sell.

(4) $P(X_1)$ = 0.69
$P(X_2)$ = 0.31

(5) EVSI = 4.0 − [(0.69)(3.5) + (0.31)(4.8)] = 0.097

b. ENGS = $970 − $500 = $470

7. See figure.

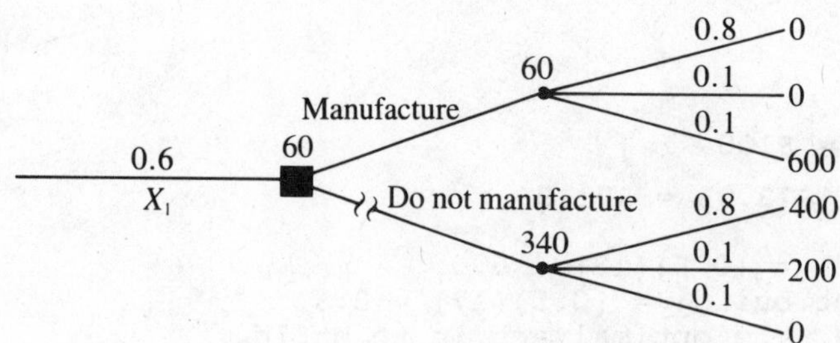

8. EVSI = 8 - 2.80 = 5.20 (tens of thousands of dollars)
EVSI = $52,000
See figure.

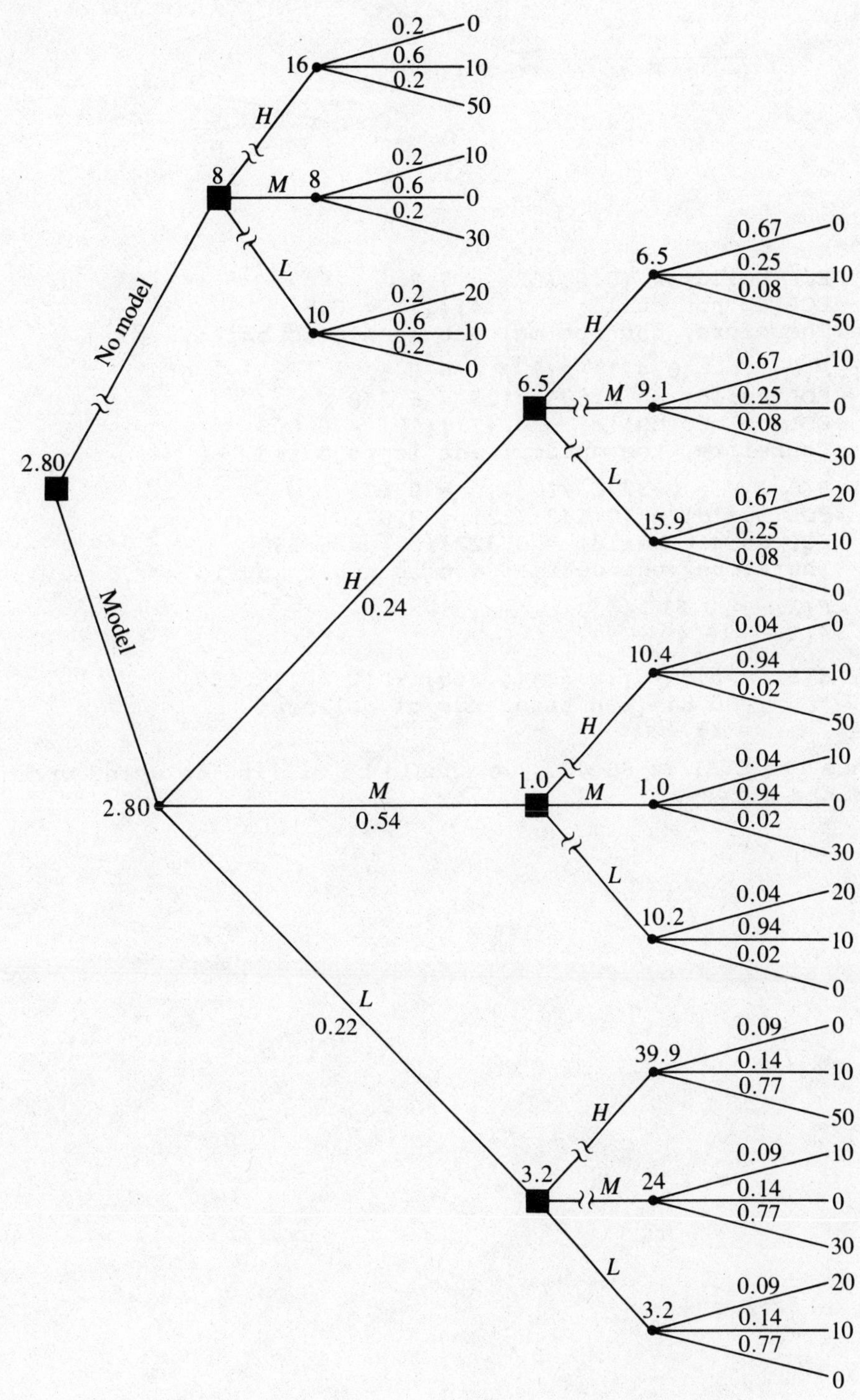

9. See figure.

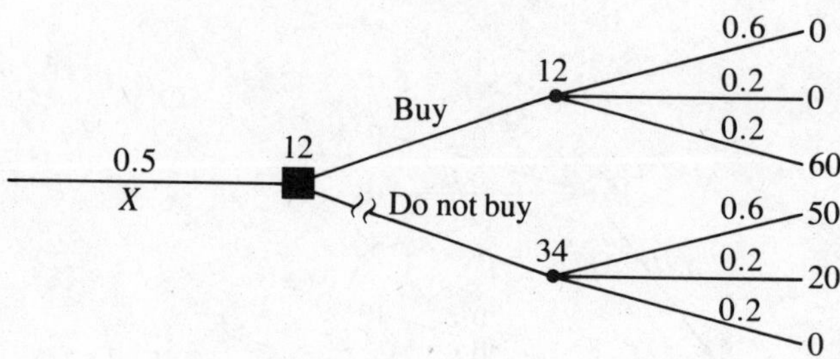

10. a. (1) EOL(build) = (0.6)(12) = 7.2
EOL(do not build) = (0.4)(17) = 6.8
Therefore, the optimal act is not to build.

(2) $P(\theta_1|X_1)$ = 0.471; $P(\theta_2|X_1)$ = 0.529
EOL(build) = (0.529)(12) = 6.348
EOL(do not build) = 0.471)(17) = 8.007
Therefore, the optimal act is to build.

(3) $P(\theta_1|X_2)$ = 0.327; $P(\theta_2|X_2)$ = 0.673
EOL(build) = (0.673)(12) = 8.075
EOL(do not build) = 0.327)(17) = 5.559
Therefore, the optimal act is not to build.

(4) $P(X_1)$ = 0.51
$P(X_2)$ = 0.49

(5) EVSI = 6.8 - [(0.51)(6.348) + (0.49)(5.559)]
= 0.84 (ten thousands of dollars)
= $8,400

b. Since the EVSI is $8,400, we should be willing to spend up to that amount for the survey.

11. EVSI = 0.9 − 0.706 = 0.194 (thousands of dollars)
See figure.

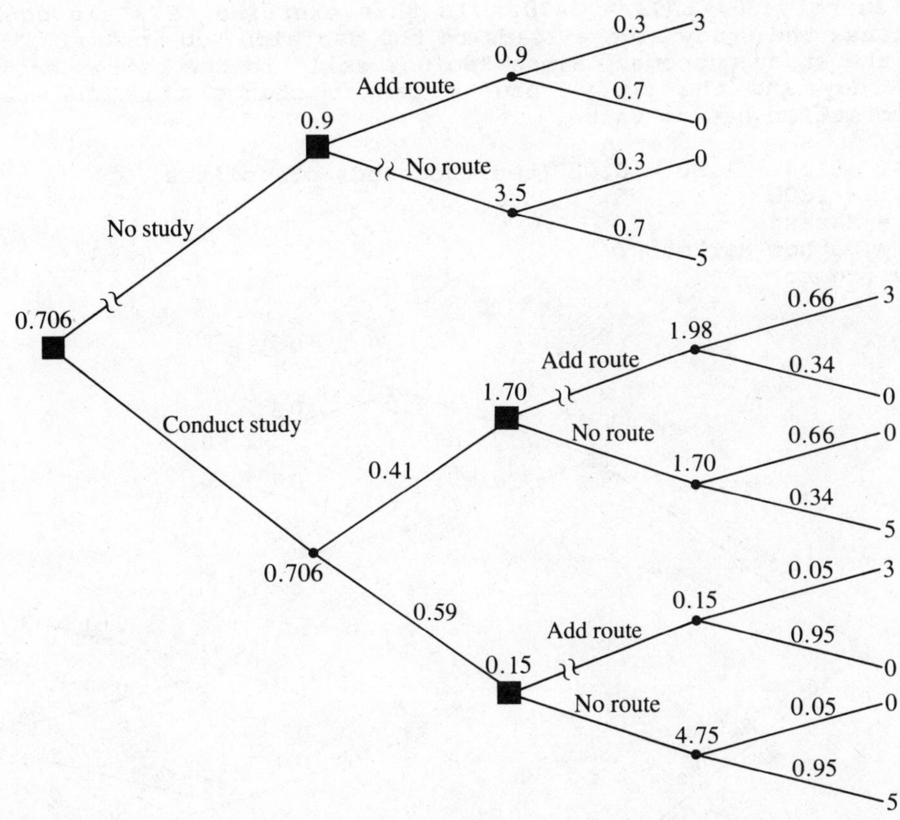

12. In this exercise, money figures are in tens of thousands of dollars.

State of Nature	$P(\theta)$	$P(X_1\|\theta)$	$P(X_2\|\theta)$	$P(\theta)P(X_1\|\theta)$	$P(\theta)P(X_2\|\theta)$	$P(\theta\|X_1)$	$P(\theta\|X_2)$
θ_1	0.70	0.75	0.25	0.525	0.175	0.745	0.593
θ_2	0.30	0.60	0.40	0.180	0.120	0.255	0.407
				$P(X_1)$ = 0.705	$P(X_2)$ = 0.295	1.000	1.000

a. (1) Without a study:
EOL(sell) = (0.70)(10) = 7.0
EOL(do not sell) = (0.30)(10) = 3.0
Therefore, the optimal act is not to sell.

(2) With information X_1 from the study:
EOL(sell) = (0.745)(10) = 7.45
EOL(do not sell) = (0.255)(10) = 2.55
Therefore, the optimal act is not to sell.

(3) With information X_2 from the study:
EOL(sell) = (0.593)(10) = 5.93
EOL(do not sell) = (0.407)(10) = 4.07
Therefore, the optimal act is not to sell.

(4) EVSI = 3.0 - [(0.750)(2.55) + (0.295)(4.07)]
= $0

(5) ENGS = $0 - $500 = -$500

b. In exercise 6, ENGS = $470. In this exercise, EVSI is equal to zero because the study always leads to the decision "do not sell," regardless of the study outcome. Since "do not sell" is the better action without a study and the study results cannot change this decision, sample information has no value.

13. a. EVSI = 1.4 - 1.32 = 0.08 (ten thousands of dollars)
= $800

M = Market

DM = Do Not Market

See figure.

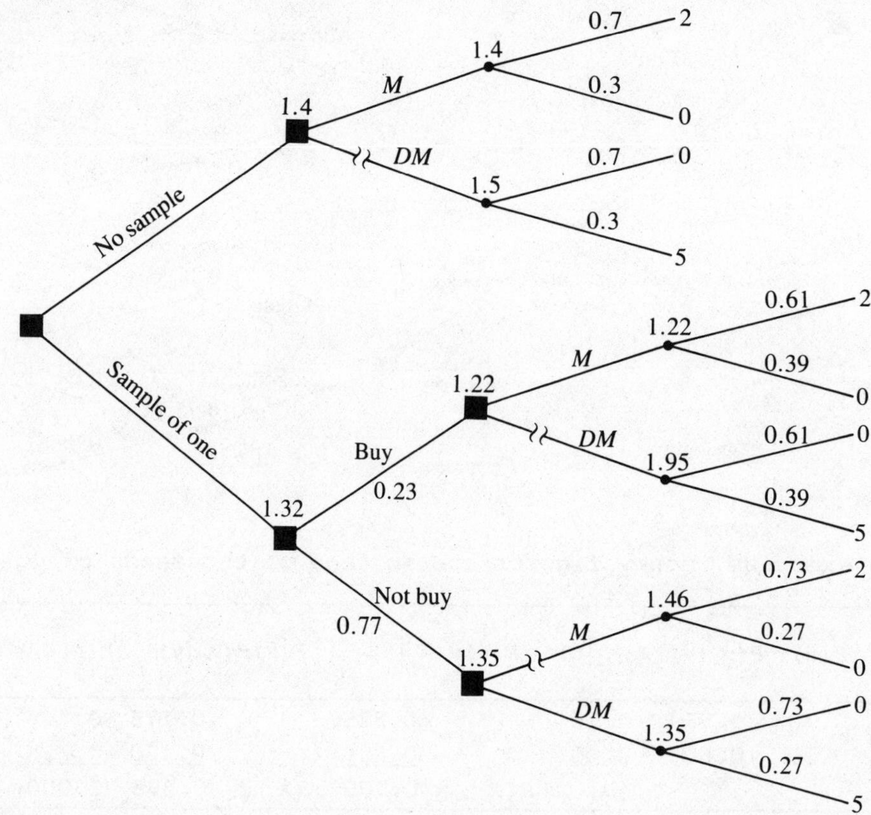

b. EVSI = 1.4 - 1.25 = 0.15 (ten thousands of dollars)
= \$1,500
See figure.

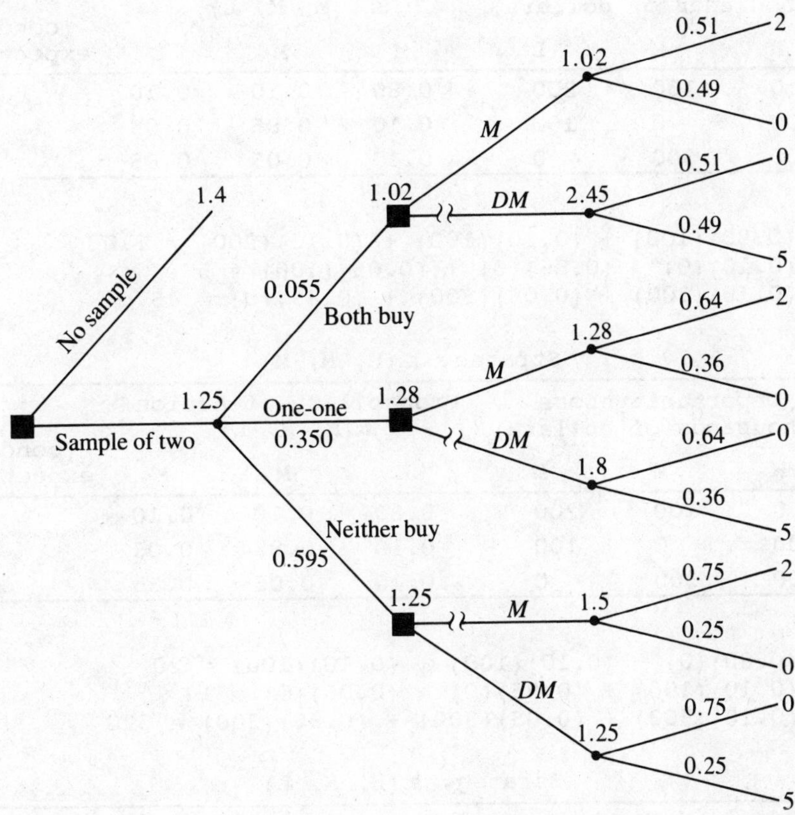

Exercises 16.4

1.

Sample Outcome	s_1	s_2	s_3	s_4	s_5	s_6	s_7	s_8
X_1	a_1	a_1	a_1	a_1	a_2	a_2	a_2	a_2
X_2	a_1	a_1	a_2	a_2	a_2	a_2	a_1	a_1
X_3	a_1	a_2	a_1	a_2	a_2	a_1	a_2	a_1

a_1 denotes "buy lot"
a_2 denotes "do not buy lot"
s_2 is the optimal strategy

2.

Sample Outcome	s_1	s_2	s_3	s_4	s_5	s_6	s_7	s_8
X	a_1	a_1	a_1	a_1	a_2	a_2	a_2	a_2
Y	a_1	a_1	a_2	a_2	a_2	a_2	a_1	a_1
Z	a_1	a_2	a_1	a_2	a_2	a_1	a_2	a_1

a_1 denotes "manufacture Crunchie Munchies"
a_2 denotes "do not manufacture Crunchie Munchies"
s_2 is the optimal strategy

3. L = Low   M = Medium   H = High

Strategy s_1(M, M, L)

State of Nature	Opportunity Loss (thousands of dollars)			Probability of Action s_1 (M, M, L)			Risk (conditional expected loss)
	H	M	L	M	M	L	
H	0	100	200	0.80	0.10	0.10	110
M	100	0	100	0.10	0.85	0.05	5
L	500	300	0	0.10	0.05	0.85	45

$R(s_1|H) = (0.80)(100) + (0.10)(100) + (0.10)(200) = 110$
$R(s_1|M) = (0.10)(0) + (0.85)(0) + (0.05)(100) = 5$
$R(s_1|L) = (0.10)(300) + (0.05)(300) + (0.85)(0) = 45$

Strategy s_2(H, M, M)

State of Nature	Opportunity Loss (thousands of dollars)			Probability of Action s_2(M, M, L)			Risk (conditional expected loss)
	H	M	L	H	M	M	
H	0	100	200	0.80	0.10	0.10	20
M	100	0	100	0.10	0.85	0.05	10
L	500	300	0	0.10	0.05	0.85	320

$R(s_2|H) = (0.80)(0) + (0.10)(100) + (0.10)(100) = 20$
$R(s_2|M) = (0.10)(100) + (0.85)(0) + (0.05)(0) = 10$
$R(s_2|L) = (0.10)(500) + (0.05)(300) + (0.85)(300) = 320$

Strategy s_3(H, M, L)

State of Nature	Opportunity Loss (thousands of dollars)			Probability of Action s_3(H, M, L)			Risk (conditional expected loss)
	H	M	L	H	M	L	
H	0	100	200	0.80	0.10	0.10	30
M	100	0	100	0.10	0.85	0.05	15
L	500	300	0	0.10	0.05	0.85	65

$R(s_3|H) = (0.80)(0) + (0.10)(100) + (0.10)(200) = 30$
$R(s_3|M) = (0.10)(100) + (0.85)(0) + (0.05)(100) = 15$
$R(s_3|L) = (0.10)(500) + (0.05)(300) + (0.85)(0) = 65$

Expected opportunity losses of the three strategies (thousands of dollars):

Strategy	Expected Opportunity Loss
s_1	(0.2)(110) + (0.6)(5) + (0.2)(45) = 34
s_2	(0.2)(20) + (0.6)(10) + (0.2)(320) = 74
s_3	(0.2)(30) + (0.6)((15) + (0.2)(65) = 28

Therefore, s_3 is the optimal strategy.

4.

Sample Outcome	s_1	s_2	s_3	s_4
Less than 25 people	a_1	a_1	a_2	a_2
25 people of more	a_2	a_1	a_2	a_1

Strategy $s_1(a_1, a_2)$

State of Nature	(thousands of dollars)		Probability of Action $s_1(a_1, a_2)$		Conditional Expected Payoff
	a_1	a_2	a_1	a_2	
Less than 25 people	-3	0	0.1	0.8	-0.3
25 people or more	5	0	0.9	0.2	4.5

Strategy $s_4(a_2, a_1)$

State of Nature	(thousands of dollars)		Probability of Action $s_4(a_2, a_1)$		Conditional Expected Payoff
	a_1	a_2	a_2	a_1	
Less than 25 people	-3	0	0.1	0.8	-2.4
25 people or more	5	0	0.9	0.2	1.0

Expected payoffs of the two strategies (thousands of dollars):

Strategy	Expected payoffs
s_1	(0.30)(-0.3) + (0.70)(4.5) = 3.06
s_4	(0.30)(-2.4) + (0.70)(1.0) = -0.02

Strategy s_1 is optimal.

5. Calculation of risks or conditional expected opportunity:

Losses for strategies s_3 and s_5

Strategy $s_3(a_1, a_2, a_2)$

Event	Opportunity Loss of Wrong Act	Probability of Wrong Act	Risk (conditional expected loss)
θ_1	1,300	0.4	520
θ_2	300	0.10	30
θ_3	800	0.10	80

Strategy $s_5(a_1, a_1, a_2)$

Event	Opportunity Loss of Wrong Act	Probability of Wrong Act	Risk (conditional expected loss)
θ_1	1,300	0.20	260
θ_2	300	0.60	180
θ_3	800	0.20	160

Expected opportunity losses of the two strategies:

Strategy	Expected Opportunity Loss
s_3	(0.35)(520) + (0.30)(30) + (0.35)(80) = 219
s_5	(0.35)(260) + (0.30)(180) + (0.35)(160) = 201

Therefore, s_5 is the optimal strategy.

Exercises 16.6

1.

State of Nature	$P_0(\theta_i)$	Probability That Four Critics Like the Book	$P_1(\theta_i)$
θ_1(successful)	p	$\binom{10}{6}(0.5)^4(0.5)^6 = 0.205$	$\frac{0.205p}{0.205p + 0.088(1-p)}$
θ_2(unsuccessful)	$1 - p$	$\binom{10}{6}(0.2)^4(0.8)^6 = 0.088$	$\frac{0.088(1-p)}{0.205p + 0.088(1-p)}$

Decision would change at

Payoff(θ_1) + Payoff(θ_2) = 0
$8(0.205p) + (-4)(0.088)(1 - p) = 0$

For $p = 0.177$, Trivia Press, Inc., would be indifferent between publishing the novel or not. For $p > 0.177$, it would be desirable to publish the novel. For $p < 0.177$, it would not be desirable to publish it.

2. ENGS = \$200 - \$167.14 - \$9.00 = \$23.86

Decision Rule

If 0 defective, then ship
If 1 defective, then ship
If 2 defective, then scrap
If 3 defective, then scrap

See figure (p. 143).

3.
$$\begin{aligned} p(50) + (1 - p)(100) &= p(70) + (1 - p)(40) \\ 100 - 50p &= 40 + 30p \\ 80p &= 60 \\ p &= 0.75 \end{aligned}$$

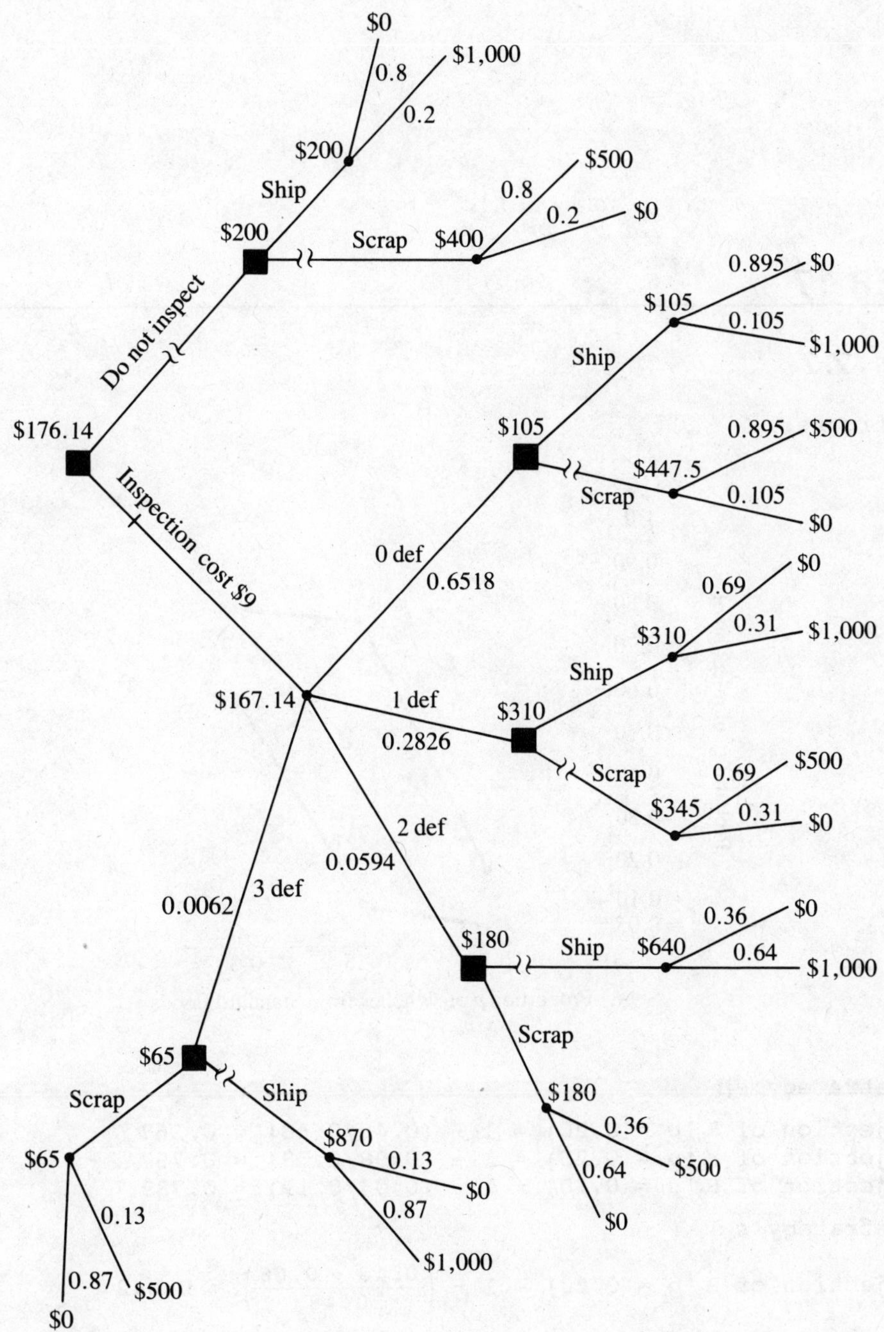

$176.14
Do not inspect
Inspection cost $9
$200
Ship
Scrap
$200
0.8
0.2
$0
$1,000
$400
0.8
0.2
$500
$0
$167.14
0 def
0.6518
1 def
0.2826
2 def
0.0594
3 def
0.0062
$105
Ship
Scrap
$105
0.895
0.105
$0
$1,000
$447.5
0.895
0.105
$500
$0
$310
Ship
Scrap
$310
0.69
0.31
$0
$1,000
$345
0.69
0.31
$500
$0
$180
Ship
Scrap
$640
0.36
0.64
$0
$1,000
$180
0.36
0.64
$500
$0
$65
Scrap
Ship
$65
0.13
0.87
$500
$0
$870
0.13
0.87
$0
$1,000

CHAPTER 17

Exercises 17.2

1. See figure.

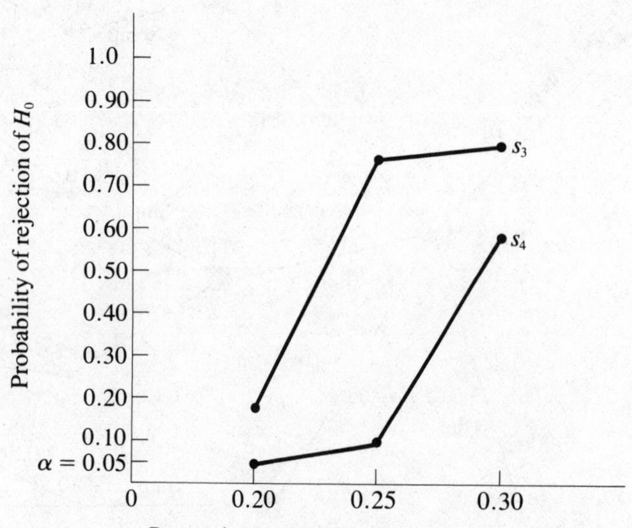

For strategy s_3:

$P(\text{rejection of } H_0 \mid p = 0.20) = 1 - (0.40/0.48) = 0.167$
$P(\text{rejection of } H_0 \mid p = 0.25) = 1 - (0.08/0.33) = 0.757$
$P(\text{rejection of } H_0 \mid p = 0.30) = 1 - (0.04/0.19) = 0.789$

For strategy s_4:

$$P(\text{rejection of } H_0 \mid p = 0.20) = 1 - \left(\frac{0.40 + 0.06}{0.48}\right) = 0.042$$

$$P(\text{rejection of } H_0 \mid p = 0.25) = 1 - \left(\frac{0.08 + 0.22}{0.33}\right) = 0.091$$

$$P(\text{rejection of } H_0 \mid p = 0.30) = 1 - \left(\frac{0.04 + 0.04}{0.19}\right) = 0.579$$

For strategy s_4, the probability of a Type I error is $0.042 < 0.05$. Therefore, s_4 satisfies the requirement.

2. a. $P(p = 0.20 \mid \overline{p} \leq c_1) = 0.40/0.52 = 0.769$

$P(p = 0.20 \mid c_1 < \overline{p} \leq c_2) = 0.06/0.32 = 0.187$

$P(p = 0.20 \mid \overline{p} > c_2) = 0.02/0.16 = 0.125$

$P(p = 0.25|\overline{p} \le c_1) = 0.08/0.52 = 0.154$

$P(p = 0.25|c_1 < \overline{p} \le c_2) = 0.22/0.32 = 0.688$

$P(p = 0.25|\overline{p} > c_2) = 0.03/0.16 = 0.188$

$P(p = 0.30|\overline{p} \le c_1) = 0.04/0.52 = 0.077$

$P(p = 0.30|c_1 < \overline{p} \le c_2) = 0.04/0.32 = 0.125$

$P(p = 0.30|\overline{p} > c_2) = 0.11/0.16 = 0.687$

b. See figure.

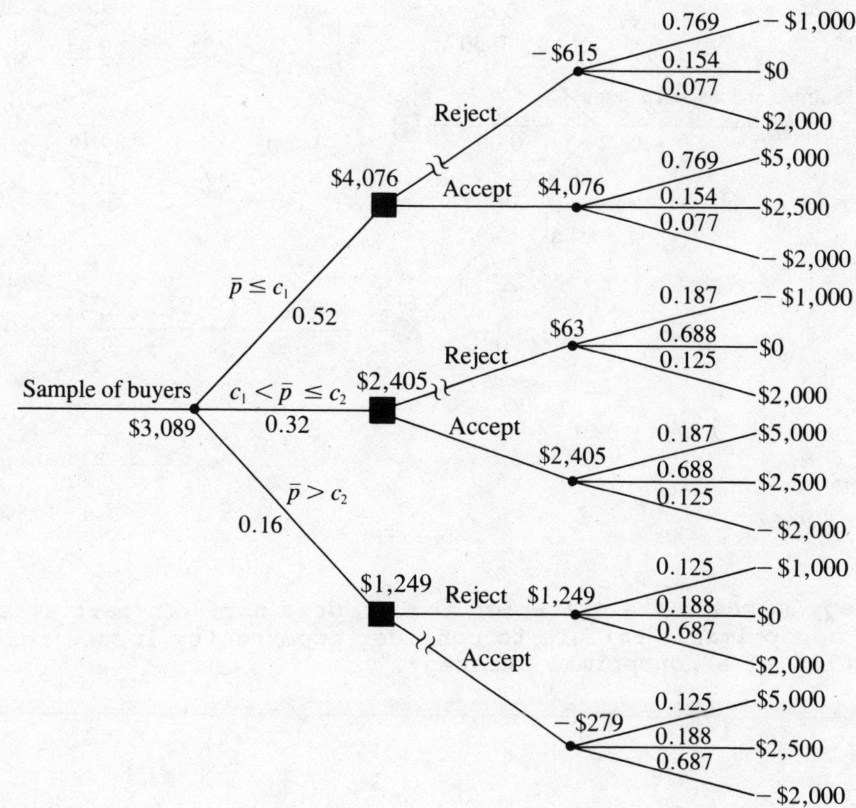

3. a. See figure. If type *M* information is observed, the optimal decision is to reject the shipment.

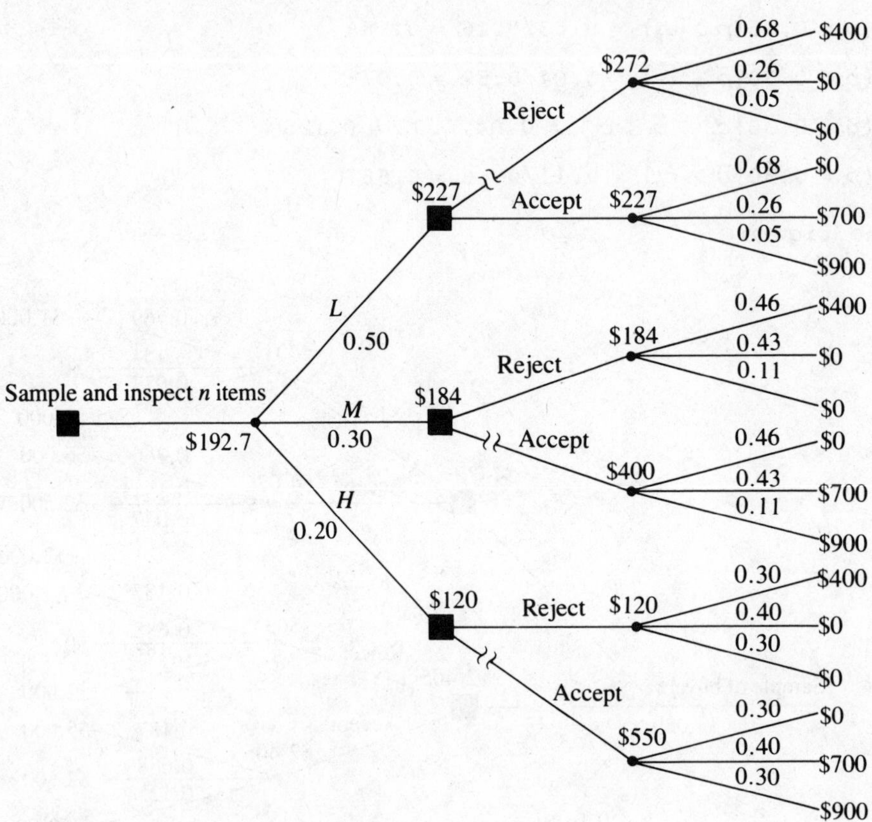

b. Strategy s_3 meets the criterion, but s_4 does not. In part a, s_3 was shown to be nonoptimal. Failure to consider opportunity losses results in the selection of a nonoptimal strategy.

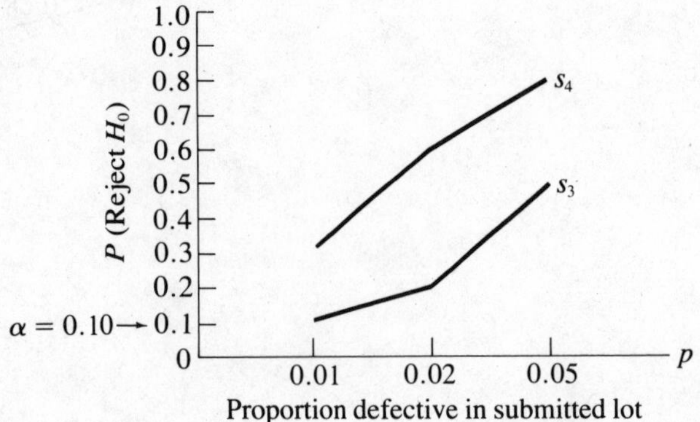

SOLUTIONS TO MINITAB EXERCISES

This file contains solutions to computer problems 1 through 4 in Chapter 1. Filename: abort.ans

Problem 1:

```
MTB > describe c1 c2

                 N      MEAN    MEDIAN    TRMEAN     STDEV    SEMEAN
ABORT81         51     384.0     356.0     359.6     242.8      34.0
ABORT85         51     368.6     333.0     351.4     193.6      27.1

               MIN       MAX        Q1        Q3
ABORT81       94.0    1627.0     239.0     476.0
ABORT85      116.0    1186.0     240.0     458.0
```

Note: there is a clear indication that the number of abortions decreased from 1981 to 1985.

Problem 2:

```
MTB > let k1=(sum(signs(c2-c1))+50)/2
MTB > print k1
K1       21.000
```

Note: Define
  m=number of states in which the number of abortions increased.
  n=number of states in which the number of abortions decreased.
    Then,   m - n = sum(signs(c2-c1))
             m + n = 50
    We can solve for m from the above equations. m = 21. Note that the number of abortions remained the same in one state.

Problem 3:

```
MTB > print c1 and c2
      (computer output omitted)

MTB > plot c2 against c1
```

```
         -                                                      *
         -
     1050+
         -
 ABORT85 -
         -
         -                          *
      700+                      *
         -                 *    *  *
         -                   2*
         -                 * ***
         -               32*
      350+            342
         -       2 3 3 2
         -     * 2 3 *
         -    22**
         -

+---------+---------+---------+---------+---------+------ABORT81
           0       300       600       900     1200      1500
```

Note: c1 and c2 appear to have a linear relationship.

Problem 4:

```
MTB > boxplot c1

                   ---------
              -----I   +   I---------                           O
                   ---------

+---------+---------+---------+---------+---------+------ABORT81
           0       300       600       900     1200      1500

MTB > boxplot c2

                   ------------
             ------I    +     I--------------                   O
                   ------------

------+---------+---------+---------+---------+---------+ABORT85
               200       400       600       800     1000   1200
```

Note: The outliers occur in the same state.

This file contains solutions to the computer problems 5 through 8 in Chapter 1. Filename: mstat.ans

---

Problem 5:

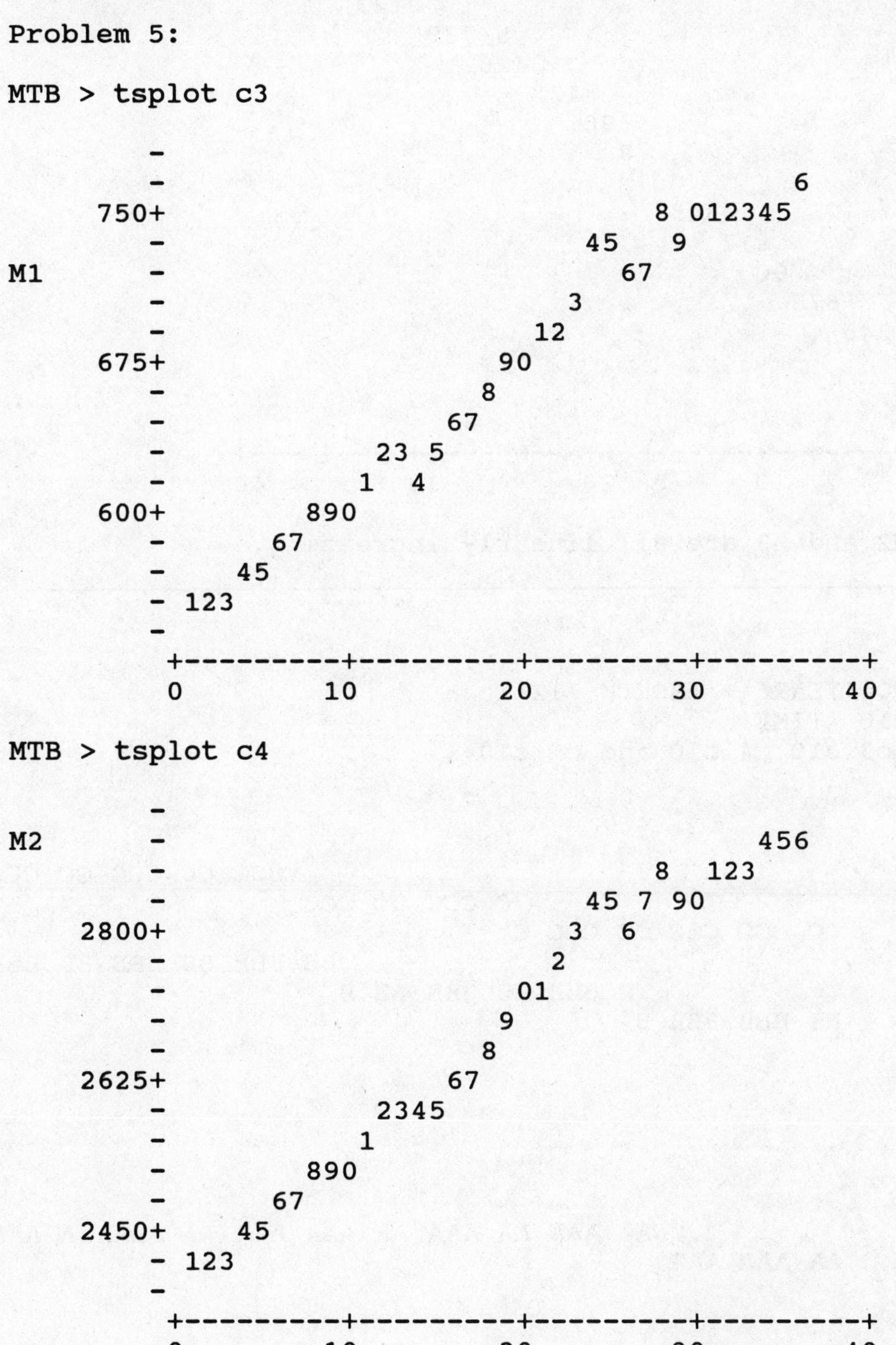

```
MTB > tsplot c3

        -
        -                                    6
     750+                           8 012345
        -                       45    9
M1      -                         67
        -                      3
        -                    12
     675+                  90
        -                 8
        -               67
        -           23 5
        -          1  4
     600+       890
        -     67
        -   45
        - 123
        -
         +---------+---------+---------+---------+
         0        10        20        30        40

MTB > tsplot c4

        -
M2      -                                 456
        -                           8  123
        -                       45 7 90
    2800+                      3  6
        -                     2
        -                   01
        -                  9
        -                 8
    2625+               67
        -           2345
        -          1
        -       890
        -     67
    2450+   45
        - 123
        -
         +---------+---------+---------+---------+
         0        10        20        30        40
```

MTB > tsplot c5

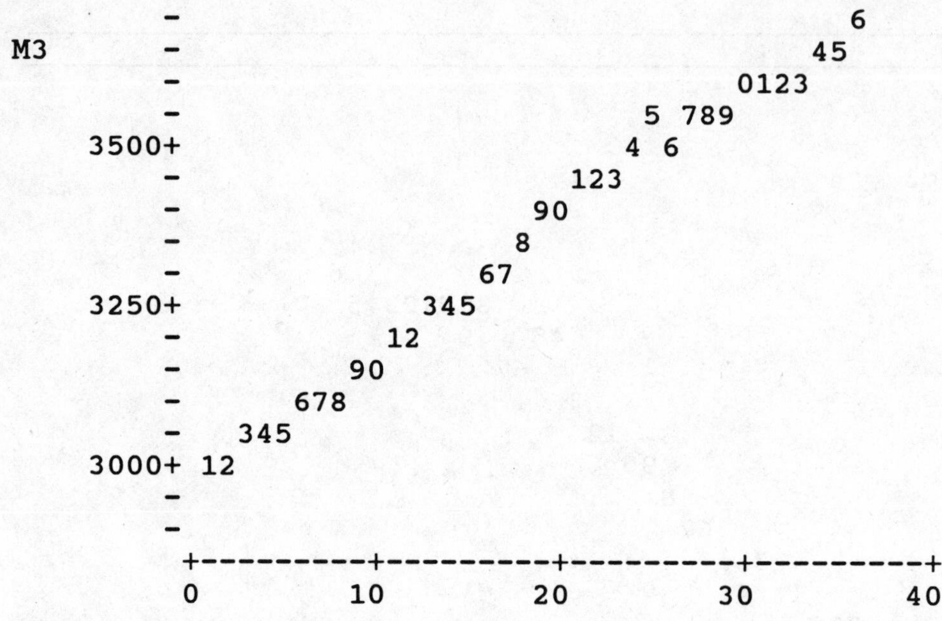

Note: M1, M2 and M3 are all linearly increasing.

Problem 6

```
MTB > let c10='YEAR' + 'MONTH'/12
MTB > name c10 'TIME'
MTB > mplot c3 c10 c4 c10 and c5 c10

          -
          -
     3600+                                        CCC CC CCC CC CCC
          -                          C CCC CC CCC
          -     CC CCC CCC CC CCC C
          -                                    BB BBB BB BBB BB BBB
          -                B BBB BB BBB BB B
     2400+      BB BBB BBB B
          -
          -
          -
          -
     1200+
          -
          -                AA AAA AA AAA AA AAA AAA AA AAA AA AAA
          -     AA AAA AAA
          -

+---------+---------+---------+---------+---------+------
     1984.80   1985.40   1986.00   1986.60   1987.20   1987.80

         A = M1 vs. TIME          C = M3 vs. TIME
         B = M2 vs. TIME
```

Problem 7

```
MTB > let c13=(c3-lag(c3))/lag(c3)
MTB > plot c13 c10

           -                                       *
C13        -                                            *
           -                          *
           -     *  *       *           *
    0.025+                                   *
           -                        *
           -             *               *                 *
           -    *   *  *                 * **       *         *
           -          *  *                             **      *
    0.000+                             *                   **
           -                                          *
           -      *           *
           -   *                                      *
           -                    *
   -0.025+
           -                                        *
           -

--------+---------+---------+---------+---------+--------TIME
           1985.40   1986.00   1986.60   1987.20   1987.80

        N* = 1
```

Note: The money supply is very volatile.

Problem 8

```
MTB > stem-and-leaf c13
Stem-and-leaf of C13         N  = 35
Leaf Unit = 0.0010           N* =  1

     1   -2 7
     2   -2 1
     4   -1 66
     5   -1 0
     6   -0 9
     9   -0 422
    13    0 0334
   (5)    0 56788
    17    1 111123
    11    1 558
     8    2 4
     7    2 7799
     3    3
     3    3 6
     2    4 03
```

```
MTB > describe c13

                  N        N*      MEAN    MEDIAN    TRMEAN     STDEV
SEMEAN
 C13             35         1   0.00907   0.00898   0.00913   0.01708
0.00289

                MIN       MAX        Q1        Q3
 C13       -0.02766   0.04383  -0.00232   0.01876
```

Note: The data are slightly skewed to the right.

This file contains solutions to the computer problems 9 through 11 in Chapter 1. Filename: bankroa.ans

---

Problem 9:

```
MTB > describe c1

                   N      MEAN    MEDIAN    TRMEAN     STDEV    SEMEAN
BANKROA          193    0.7010    0.9000    0.7659    0.7191    0.0518

                 MIN       MAX        Q1        Q3
BANKROA      -2.8000    2.3000    0.5000    1.1000

MTB > let k1=stdev(c1)/mean(c1)
MTB > print k1
K1       1.02574, which is the coefficient of variation.
```

Problem 10

```
MTB > let k1=sum(absolute(c1-median(c1)))
MTB > let k2=sum(absolute(c1-mean(c1)))
MTB > print k1 k2
K1       87.6001
K2       90.5700
```

Note: it is true that k1 < k2.

Problem 11

```
MTB > dotplot c1

                                                  .
                                                 .:
                                               : ::
                                               : :: :
                                               : :: :
                                             . ::::.:
                                             : ::::::
                                             :.::::::
                                          : :::::::::.
                               .          : ::::::::::.
                               :       :  : :::::::::::    :
            :   .         ..   :.... ..:::: ::::::::::::...:   .

+---------+---------+---------+---------+---------+---------+-------BANKROA

      -3.0      -2.0      -1.0       0.0       1.0       2.0
```

```
MTB > histogram c1

Histogram of BANKROA   N = 193
Each * represents 2 obs.

Midpoint   Count
    -3.0       2  *
    -2.5       1  *
    -2.0       0
    -1.5       2  *
    -1.0       6  ***
    -0.5       4  **
     0.0      17  *********
     0.5      50  *************************
     1.0      89  *********************************************
     1.5      16  ********
     2.0       5  ***
     2.5       1  *
```

Note: The data are skewed to the left. The median (0.9000) is greater than the mean (0.7010), and the left tail of the distribution is longer than the right tail.

This file contains solutions to computer problems in Chapter 3.
Filename: discrete.ans

Problem 1:

```
MTB > set c1
DATA> 0:20
MTB > end

MTB > pdf c1 c2;
SUBC> binomial 20 0.4.
MTB > print c1 c2

 ROW    C1        C2

   1     0   0.000037
   2     1   0.000487
   3     2   0.003087
   4     3   0.012350
   5     4   0.034991
   6     5   0.074647
   7     6   0.124412
   8     7   0.165882
   9     8   0.179706
  10     9   0.159738
  11    10   0.117142
  12    11   0.070995
  13    12   0.035497
  14    13   0.014563
  15    14   0.004854
  16    15   0.001294
  17    16   0.000270
  18    17   0.000042
  19    18   0.000005
  20    19   0.000001
  21    20   0.000001
```

Note: Mode = 8

```
MTB > plot c2 c1
```

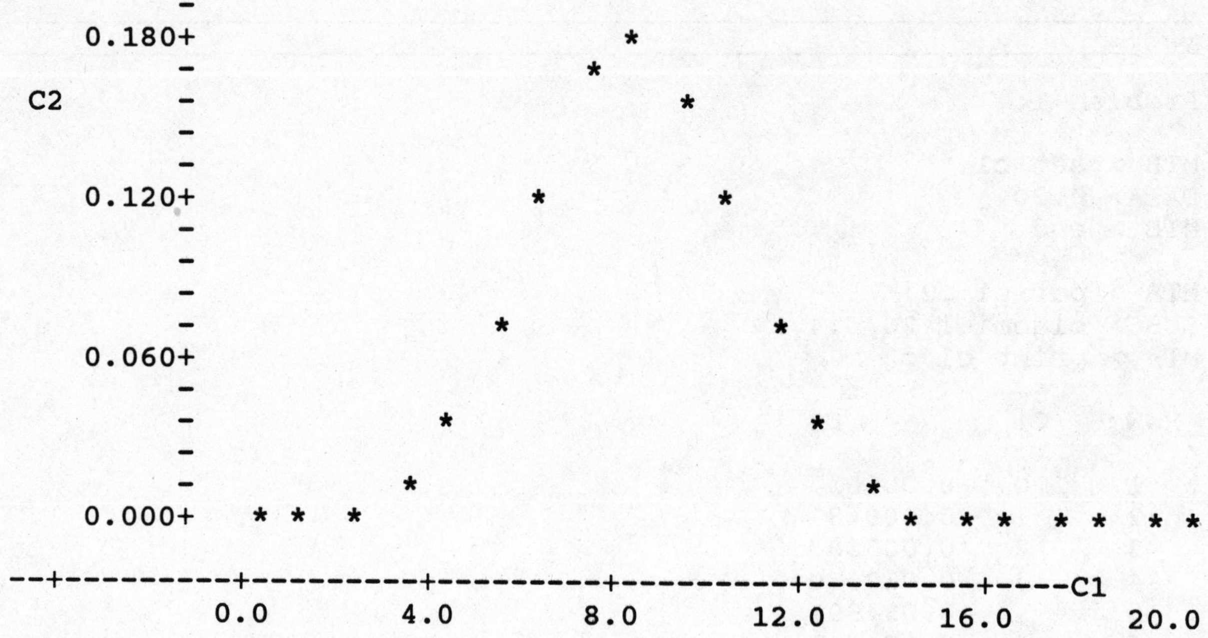

```
MTB > cdf c1 c3;
SUBC> binomial 20 0.4.
MTB > print c1 c2 c3
```

ROW	C1	C2	C3
1	0	0.000037	0.00004
2	1	0.000487	0.00052
3	2	0.003087	0.00361
4	3	0.012350	0.01596
5	4	0.034991	0.05095
6	5	0.074647	0.12560
7	6	0.124412	0.25001
8	7	0.165882	0.41589
9	8	0.179706	0.59560
10	9	0.159738	0.75534
11	10	0.117142	0.87248
12	11	0.070995	0.94347
13	12	0.035497	0.97897
14	13	0.014563	0.99353
15	14	0.004854	0.99839
16	15	0.001294	0.99968
17	16	0.000270	0.99995
18	17	0.000042	0.99999
19	18	0.000005	1.00000
20	19	0.000001	1.00000
21	20	0.000001	1.00000

```
Note: Median=8
MTB > let k1=sum(c1*C2)
MTB > print k1
K1        8.00003, which is the mean.
Note: k1 > 8, because of rounding error.
```

Problem 2:

```
MTB > set c1
DATA> 0:25
MTB > end

MTB > pdf c1 c2;
SUBC> poisson 6.
MTB > pdf c1 c3;
SUBC> poisson 10.
MTB > print c1 c2 c3
```

ROW	C1	C2	C3
1	0	0.002479	0.000045
2	1	0.014873	0.000454
3	2	0.044618	0.002270
4	3	0.089235	0.007567
5	4	0.133853	0.018917
6	5	0.160623	0.037833
7	6	0.160623	0.063055
8	7	0.137677	0.090079
9	8	0.103258	0.112599
10	9	0.068838	0.125110
11	10	0.041303	0.125110
12	11	0.022529	0.113736
13	12	0.011264	0.094780
14	13	0.005199	0.072908
15	14	0.002228	0.052077
16	15	0.000891	0.034718
17	16	0.000334	0.021699
18	17	0.000118	0.012764
19	18	0.000039	0.007091
20	19	0.000012	0.003732
21	20	0.000004	0.001866
22	21	0.000001	0.000889
23	22	0.000001	0.000404
24	23	0.000001	0.000176
25	24	0.000001	0.000073
26	25	0.000001	0.000029

```
MTB > mplot c2 c1 c3 c1

         -
    0.180+
         -
         -           A A
         -
         -         A     A
    0.120+                   B B
         -                 2     B
         -               B         B
         -       A
         -                   A       B
    0.060+             B
         -     A                       B
         -           B         A         B
         -         B             A         B
         -   A   B                 A         B B
    0.000+ 2 B B                     A A A A A A 2 2 2 2 2 2 2

+---------+---------+---------+---------+---------+------
         0.0       5.0      10.0      15.0      20.0      25.0

         A = C2 vs. C1                 B = C3 vs. C1
```

Note: When the mean is increased, the density function is shifted to the right.

Note: Mode = 5 or 6

```
MTB > cdf c1 c3;
SUBC> poisson 6.

MTB > print c1 c3
```

ROW	C1	C3
1	0	0.00248
2	1	0.01735
3	2	0.06197
4	3	0.15120
5	4	0.28506
6	5	0.44568
7	6	0.60630
8	7	0.74398
9	8	0.84724
10	9	0.91608
11	10	0.95738
12	11	0.97991
13	12	0.99117
14	13	0.99637
15	14	0.99860
16	15	0.99949
17	16	0.99983

```
18    17   0.99994
19    18   0.99998
20    19   0.99999
21    20   1.00000
22    21   1.00000
23    22   1.00000
24    23   1.00000
25    24   1.00000
26    25   1.00000
```

Note: Median = 6

```
MTB > let k1=sum(c1*c2)
MTB > print k1
K1       6.00008, which is the mean.

MTB > let k2=sum(c2*((c1-k1)**2))
MTB > print k2
K2       6.00113, which is the variance.
```

Note: The calculated mean is equal to the variance except for rounding error.

This file contains solutions to computer exercises in Chapter 5. Filename: random.ans

---

Problem 1:

```
MTB > random 60 c1;
SUBC> binomial 70 0.3.

MTB > nscore c1 c2
MTB > plot c2 c1

C2       -                                                  *
         -
         -
    1.5+                                               4
         -                                         2
         -                                     4
         -                                 5
         -                         6   7
    0.0+                       7
         -                 4
         -         4   3
         -     6
         -
   -1.5+   6
         -
         -
         - *

+---------+---------+---------+---------+---------+------C1
        15.0      17.5      20.0      22.5      25.0      27.5
```

Note: The above plot looks like a straight line. Your plot can be different from the above, due to randomness.

Problem 2:

```
MTB > random 30 c1;
SUBC> normal 0 1.

MTB > parsum c1 c2

MTB > let c3=expo(c2)

MTB > set c4
DATA> 1:30
MTB > end
```

```
MTB > plot c3 c4
     12.0+
         -                         *
C3       -
         -
         -                          *
      8.0+
         -             *                *
         -
         -                *      *
         -               *            *
      4.0+           *                       *
         -          *
         -                               *
         -        *            *
         -     **           * *            *  * * *  *
      0.0+                                         *   ** * ** *
         -

--+---------+---------+---------+---------+---------+----C4
           0.0       6.0      12.0      18.0      24.0      30.0
```

This file contains solutions to Review Problems for Chapter 1 through Chapter 5. Filename: rev1-5.ans

---

Problem 1:

```
MTB > set c1
DATA> 16:20
MTB > end

MTB > pdf c1 c2;
SUBC> binomial 30 0.6.

MTB > let k1=sum(c2)
MTB > print k1
K1      0.648344
```

Note: 30 days later, the probability that the price was in the range of 42 to 52 is 0.648344.

Problem 2:

```
MTB > random 30 c1;
SUBC> Bernoulli 0.6.

MTB > let c1=2*(c1-0.5)
MTB > let c2=40+parsums(c1)

MTB > tsplot c2


    44.00+                        4
         -
C2       -                      3 5   9
         -
         -
    42.00+                   8   2   6 8 0
         -
         -       7          7 9 1     7
         -
         -
    40.00+    4 6 8   2 4 6   0
         -
         - 1 3 5   9 1 3 5
         -
         -
    38.00+  2       0
         -
          +---------+---------+---------+
          0        10        20        30
```

Note: There were 16 days in which the stock prices increased.

Problem 3:

```
MTB > describe c1 c2

                 N      MEAN    MEDIAN    TRMEAN     STDEV    SEMEAN
PROA            30    0.1717    0.1800    0.1685    0.0606    0.0111
PROB            25    0.1744    0.1500    0.1717    0.1272    0.0254

               MIN       MAX        Q1        Q3
PROA        0.0600    0.3200    0.1350    0.1950
PROB        0.0100    0.4000    0.0500    0.3200
```

Note: Since the mean of PROB > mean of PROA, the investor will invest in Project B.

Problem 4:

Note: Since the median of PROA > median of PROB, the investor is going to invest in Project A.

Problem 5:

	mean + sqrt(variance)
Project A	0.1717 + 0.0606 = 0.2323
Project B	0.1744 + 0.1272 = 0.3016

Note: The investor would prefer Project B.

Problem 6:

```
MTB > store 'sample'
STOR> noecho
STOR> sample 4 c1 ck1
STOR> let k2=mean(ck1)
STOR> stack c20 k2 c20
STOR> let k1=k1+1
STOR> end

MTB > let k1=2
MTB > stack 1 1 c20

MTB > execute 'sample' 16

MTB > copy c20 c20;
SUBC> omit 1 2.
```

```
MTB > describe c1 c20

              N       MEAN     MEDIAN     TRMEAN      STDEV     SEMEAN
PROA         30     0.1717     0.1800     0.1685     0.0606     0.0111
C20          16    0.18000    0.17625    0.17679    0.03142    0.00786

            MIN        MAX         Q1         Q3
PROA     0.0600     0.3200     0.1350     0.1950
C20     0.14250    0.26250    0.15438    0.19187

Histogram of C20    N = 16

Midpoint   Count
    0.14       2  **
    0.16       4  ****
    0.18       5  *****
    0.20       3  ***
    0.22       0
    0.24       1  *
    0.26       1  *
```

Note: The mean of the sample means in this empirical sampling distribution is roughly the same as the population mean, while the standard deviation of the sample means is roughly one-half of the population standard deviation. The theory predicts that in the sampling distribution of the mean, the expected value of the sample mean is equal to the population mean, and the standard deviation of the sample mean (the standard error of the mean) is equal to the population standard deviation divided by the square root of the sample size. Here the sample size=4.

Problem 7:

```
MTB > random 20 c1-c10;
SUBC> normal 0 1.

MTB > rmeans of c1-c10, put into c20

MTB > describe c20

              N       MEAN     MEDIAN     TRMEAN      STDEV     SEMEAN
C20          20    -0.0317    -0.0121    -0.0345     0.3706     0.0829

            MIN        MAX         Q1         Q3
C20     -0.7144     0.7027    -0.3666     0.2786
```

Note: The mean and standard deviation of the standard normal distribution are 0 and 1, respectively. The mean of the sample means is almost 0, while the standard deviation of the sample means, 0.3706, is roughly 1 divided by the square root of 10.

Problem 8:

```
MTB > describe c1

                 N      MEAN    MEDIAN    TRMEAN     STDEV    SEMEAN
SERV A          80     9.488     9.000     9.444     3.708     0.415

               MIN       MAX        Q1        Q3
SERV A       1.000    17.000     7.000    12.000
```

Note: The mean=9.488 > median=9.000. Variance=(square of 3.708) = 13.75, is larger than the mean.

Problem 9:

```
MTB > random 80 c3;
SUBC> Poisson 9.488.

MTB > dotplot c1 c3;
SUBC> same.
```

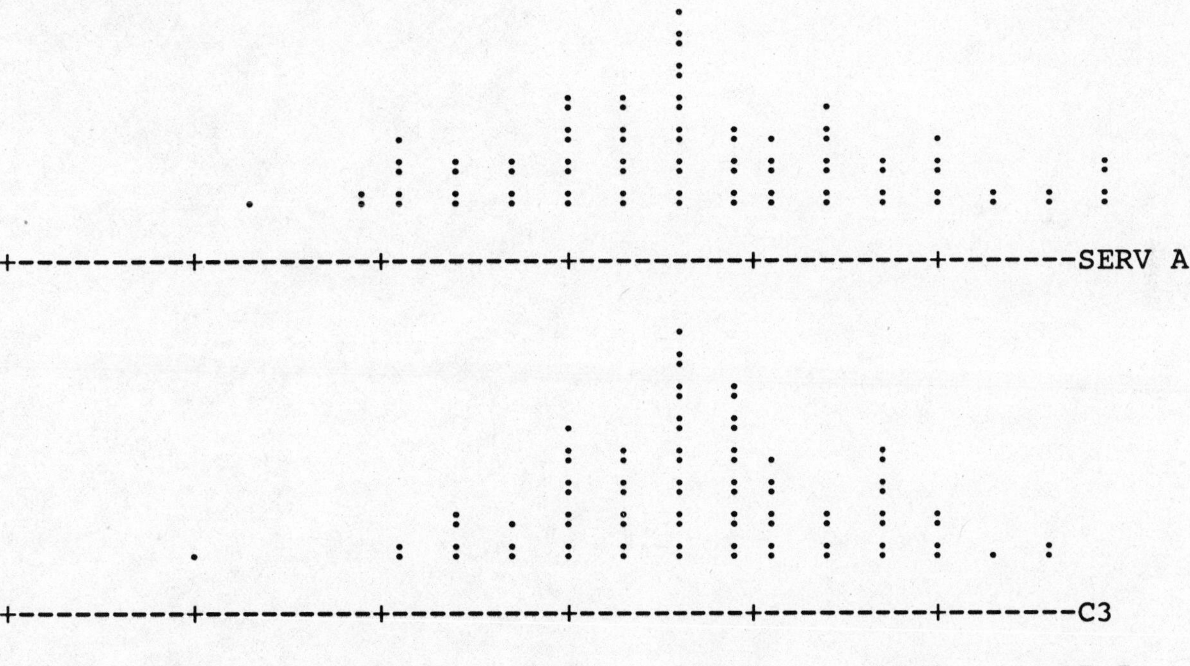

Note: The above dotplots are quite similar in appearance.

Problem 10:

MTB > describe c1 and c2

	N	MEAN	MEDIAN	TRMEAN	STDEV	SEMEAN
SERV A	80	9.488	9.000	9.444	3.708	0.415
SERV B	80	7.950	7.500	7.903	2.671	0.299

	MIN	MAX	Q1	Q3
SERV A	1.000	17.000	7.000	12.000
SERV B	0.000	15.000	6.000	10.000

Note: On average, SERV A attracts more customers that SERV B. The relative variabilities, as measured by the coefficient of variation, are

CV1 = 3.708/9.488 = 0.39 for SERV A; and
CV2 = 2.671/7.950 = 0.34 for SERV B.

Thus C1 is relatively more variable than C2 in the above sense.

This file contains solutions to computer problems in Chapter 6.
Filename: roa.ans

Problem 1:

```
MTB > desc c1 c2

                 N      MEAN    MEDIAN    TRMEAN     STDEV    SEMEAN
BANKROA        193    0.7010    0.9000    0.7659    0.7191    0.0518
AIRROA          43     2.058     2.400     2.000     4.411     0.673

               MIN       MAX        Q1        Q3
BANKROA    -2.8000    2.3000    0.5000    1.1000
AIRROA      -5.900    13.800    -1.200     5.300

MTB > let
k1=(2.058-0.7010)-2.58*sqrt((0.7191**2)/193+(4.411**2)/43)

MTB > let
k2=(2.058-0.7010)+2.58*sqrt((0.7191**2)/193+(4.411**2)/43)

MTB > print k1 k2
K1        -0.383622
K2        3.09762
```

Note: The desired confidence interval is (-0.3836, 3.0976).

Problem 2:

```
MTB > zinterval 95% 0.6 c1

THE ASSUMED SIGMA =0.600

              N      MEAN     STDEV  SE MEAN    95.0 PERCENT C.I.
BANKROA     193    0.7010    0.7191   0.0432   (  0.6163,   0.7858)


MTB > zinterval 95% 4.5 c2

THE ASSUMED SIGMA =4.50

              N      MEAN     STDEV  SE MEAN    95.0 PERCENT C.I.
AIRROA       43     2.058     4.411    0.686   (   0.711,    3.405)
```

Problem 3:

```
MTB > zinterval 95% 4.6 c2

THE ASSUMED SIGMA =4.60

              N      MEAN     STDEV  SE MEAN    95.0 PERCENT C.I.
AIRROA       43     2.058     4.411    0.701  (    0.681,     3.435)
```

Note: A larger standard deviation results in a wider confidence interval.

Problem 4:

```
MTB > set c10
DATA> 1.9 1.7 1.6 1.5 1.2 1.2 0.9 0.4 0.1 -0.3 -0.8 -1.3
MTB > end
MTB > tinterval 99% c10

              N      MEAN     STDEV  SE MEAN    99.0 PERCENT C.I.
C10          12     0.675     1.050    0.303  (   -0.266,     1.616)
```

Problem 5:

```
MTB > describe c3

                 N      MEAN    MEDIAN    TRMEAN     STDEV    SEMEAN
RANDOM         200    0.4750    0.0000    0.4722    0.5006    0.0354

               MIN       MAX        Q1        Q3
RANDOM      0.0000    1.0000    0.0000    1.0000

MTB > let k1=0.475-1.65*sqrt(0.475*0.525/200)
MTB > let k2=0.475+1.65*sqrt(0.475*0.525/200)
MTB > print k1 k2
K1       0.416737
K2       0.533263
```

Note: The desired confidence interval is (0.417, 0.533). And 0.5 is in the confidence interval.

This file contains solutions to computer problems in Chapter 7.
Filename: testing.ans

Problem 1:

```
MTB > ttest mean=7 for c1

TEST OF MU = 7.000 VS MU N.E. 7.000

              N      MEAN     STDEV   SE MEAN        T     P VALUE
FOOD        100     7.364     3.651     0.365     1.00        0.32

MTB > let k1=stdev(c1)
MTB > ztest mean=7 with sigma=k1 for c1

TEST OF MU = 7.000 VS MU N.E. 7.000
THE ASSUMED SIGMA = 3.65

              N      MEAN     STDEV   SE MEAN        Z     P VALUE
FOOD        100     7.364     3.651     0.365     1.00        0.32
```

Note: Since the p value = 0.32 > 0.15, the hypothesis is tenable. The reason for the equality of the p values is that as the number of degrees of freedom becomes large (greater than 30), the t-distribution looks very much like a normal distribution.

Problem 2:
Note: Because of the symmetry of the normal distribution, the p value should be 0.32/2 = 0.16, as confirmed below:

```
MTB > ttest mean=7 for c1;
SUBC> alternative 1.

TEST OF MU = 7.000 VS MU G.T. 7.000

              N      MEAN     STDEV   SE MEAN        T     P VALUE
FOOD        100     7.364     3.651     0.365     1.00        0.16
```

Problem 3:

```
MTB > ztest 45 sigma=20 c2;
SUBC> alternative -1.

TEST OF MU = 45.000 VS MU L.T. 45.000
THE ASSUMED SIGMA = 20.0

              N      MEAN     STDEV   SE MEAN        Z     P VALUE
INCOME      100    41.720    18.983     2.000    -1.64       0.051
```

Note: Since the p value=0.051 < 0.10, reject the null hypothesis.

Problem 4:

```
MTB > boxplot c2;
SUBC> by c5.

OWNER

                                 -----------
0                     -----------I    +    I-------------               *
                                 -----------

                      ----------
1                 ----I    +   I--------              *
                      ----------

--------+---------+---------+---------+---------+--------INCOME
                 20        40        60        80       100
```

Note: There is a clear indication that the mean INCOME of families with their own homes is greater than that of families without their own homes.

Formulation of a Testing Problem:
H0: mean of c2 (c5=0) < or = mean of c2 (c5=1)
H1: mean of c2 (c5=0) > mean of c2 (c5=1)

```
MTB > twot c2, groups in c5;
SUBC> alternative -1;
SUBC> pooled.

TWOSAMPLE T FOR INCOME
OWNER    N       MEAN      STDEV    SE MEAN
1       51       30.9       12.8        1.8
0       49       52.9       17.9        2.6

95 PCT CI FOR MU 1 - MU 0: (-28.2, -15.8)

TTEST MU 1 = MU 0 (VS LT): T= -7.09  P=0.0000  DF=  98

POOLED STDEV =        15.5
```

Note: Since the p value = 0, reject H0.

Problem 5:

```
MTB > let k1=mean(1-c5)-1.96*sqrt(0.5*0.5/100)
MTB > let k2=mean(1-c5)+1.96*sqrt(0.5*0.5/100)
MTB > print k1 k2
K1       0.392000
K2       0.588000
```

Decision Rule: Retain H0 if and only if k1 < 0.5 < k2.
Conclusion: Retain H0.

This file contains solutions to computer problems in Chapter 8.
Filename: table.ans

Problem 1:

```
MTB > set c1
DATA> 116 138 125 123 132 117 121 128
DATA> end

MTB > let c2=125*(c1/c1), which is the expected frequency.

MTB > print c1 c2

 ROW     C1     C2

   1    116    125
   2    138    125
   3    125    125
   4    123    125
   5    132    125
   6    117    125
   7    121    125
   8    128    125

MTB > let k1=sum( ((c1-c2)**2)/c2 )
MTB > print k1
K1       3.13600, which is the chisquare statistic.
```

Note: Number of degrees of freedom = 7. At alpha = 0.05, the critical value = 14.067 > 3.136, so we retain H0.

Problem 2:

```
MTB > random 200 c1;
SUBC> binomial with n=3 and p=0.5.
MTB > histogram c1

Histogram of C1   N = 200
Each * represents 2 obs.

Midpoint   Count
       0      24  ************
       1      75  **************************************
       2      75  **************************************
       3      26  *************


MTB > set c1
DATA> 24 75 75 26
MTB > end
```

```
MTB > set c2
DATA> 1 3 3 1
MTB > end

MTB > let c2=c2*(200/sum(c2)), which is the expected frequency.

MTB > print c1 c2

 ROW     C1     C2

   1     24     25
   2     75     75
   3     75     75
   4     26     25

MTB > let k1=sum(((c1-c2)**2)/c2)
MTB > print k1
K1          0.0800000, which is the chisquare statistic.
```

Note: Number of degrees of freedom = 3. At alpha = 0.10, the critical value = 6.251 > 0.08, so we retain H0.

Problem 3:

```
MTB > read c1 c2 c3 c4
DATA>  994  33   476  226
DATA> 1556  86   964  308
DATA> 1614  61   887  279
DATA>  840  28  1041  415
DATA>  end

MTB > chisquare c1-c4
```

Expected counts are printed below observed counts

	C1	C2	C3	C4	Total
1	994	33	476	226	1729
	882.13	36.67	593.73	216.48	
2	1556	86	964	308	2914
	1486.71	61.80	1000.65	364.84	
3	1614	61	887	279	2841
	1449.47	60.25	975.58	355.70	
4	840	28	1041	415	2324
	1185.69	49.29	798.05	290.97	
Total	5004	208	3368	1228	9808

```
ChiSq = 14.188 +  0.367 + 23.343 +  0.419 +
         3.229 +  9.479 +  1.342 +  8.857 +
        18.677 +  0.009 +  8.043 + 16.541 +
       100.789 +  9.193 + 73.964 + 52.865 = 341.304
df = 9
```

Note: At alpha=0.01, the critical value = 21.666 < 341.304, so we reject the hypothesis of independence. If we multiply all the data by 100, then the chisquare statistic becomes 34130.4, which is 341.304 * 100.

Problem 4:

```
MTB > info

COLUMN     NAME       COUNT
C1                       30
C2                       23
C3                       28
C4                       25

CONSTANTS USED: NONE

MTB > dotplot c1-c4;
SUBC> same.

                 .   :  ::  .:.   .::  ::   .:. .. .   .  ..

-----+---------+---------+---------+---------+---------+-C1
                                  .
                   ...  .: ..:.. :..  : .  .     .  .

-----+---------+---------+---------+---------+---------+-C2
                        :    ..   .
                     .  :. ::: . : .. :: .   . .    .

-----+---------+---------+---------+---------+---------+-C3
                                  .
                     .   :   .    ::::::..:      .:   ..      .

-----+---------+---------+---------+---------+---------+-C4
              2.0       4.0       6.0       8.0      10.0      12.0
```

Note: Visually, the null hypothesis is tenable.

```
MTB > aovoneway c1-c4

ANALYSIS OF VARIANCE
SOURCE      DF        SS          MS         F        p
FACTOR       3      26.12        8.71      2.34    0.078
ERROR      102     379.53        3.72
TOTAL      105     405.65
```

Note: Since the p value > 0.05, we retain the null hypothesis.

Problem 5:

```
COLUMN     NAME       COUNT
C1         STATES       162
C2         DMOTOR       162

CONSTANTS USED: NONE

MTB > oneway for data in c2, subscripts in c1

ANALYSIS OF VARIANCE ON DMOTOR
SOURCE      DF        SS          MS         F        p
STATES       2      3881        1941     14.23    0.000
ERROR      159     21690         136
TOTAL      161     25572
```

Note: Since the p value < 0.01, we reject the null hypothesis.

Problem 6:

```
MTB > table c1 c2;
SUBC> data in c3.

 ROWS: DEGREE      COLUMNS: SEX

            0        1

   1     78.000   82.000
         83.000   84.000
         67.000   79.000

   2     87.000   70.000
         76.000   68.000
         72.000   71.000

   3     69.000   65.000
         81.000   63.000
         79.000   70.000

  CELL CONTENTS --
             LIFE:DATA
MTB > table c1 c2;
```

```
SUBC> mean of c3.


 ROWS: DEGREE     COLUMNS: SEX

              0         1       ALL

   1    76.000    81.667    78.833
   2    78.333    69.667    74.000
   3    76.333    66.000    71.167
 ALL    76.889    72.444    74.667

  CELL CONTENTS --
             LIFE:MEAN
```

Note: we can see a slight interaction between SEX and DEGREE
      from the above table.

```
MTB > twoway analysis, obs in c3, factors in c1 and c2

ANALYSIS OF VARIANCE  LIFE

SOURCE          DF         SS         MS
DEGREE           2      180.3       90.2
SEX              1       88.9       88.9
INTERACTION      2      232.1      116.1
ERROR           12      380.7       31.7
TOTAL           17      882.0
```

Note: The F statistic = 116.1/31.7 = 3.66. At alpha=0.05, the critical value = 3.88 > 3.66, so we retain the null hypothesis that no interaction exists between SEX and DEGREE.

This file contains solutions to review exercises for Chapter 6 through Chapter 8. Filename: rev6-8.ans

---

Problem 1:

```
MTB > hist c1

Histogram of VOTE   N = 500
Each * represents 5 obs.

Midpoint   Count
      -1     159  ********************************
       0     167  **********************************
       1     174  ***********************************

MTB > set c10
DATA> 159 167 174
DATA> end

MTB > let k1=500/3
MTB > set c11
DATA> k1 k1 k1
DATA> end

MTB > print c10 c11

 ROW    C10       C11

   1    159   166.667
   2    167   166.667
   3    174   166.667

MTB > let k1=sum( ((c10-c11)**2)/c11 )
MTB > print k1
K1        0.676000
```

Note: The number of degrees of freedom = 2. At alpha=0.15, we retain the null hypothesis since the critical value for alpha=0.20 is 3.219, which is larger than 0.676, the actual chi-square statistic.

Problem 2:

```
MTB > code (-1) to 0 in c1, put into c2
MTB > describe c2

               N      MEAN    MEDIAN    TRMEAN     STDEV    SEMEAN
C2           500    0.3480    0.0000    0.3311    0.4768    0.0213

             MIN       MAX        Q1        Q3
C2        0.0000    1.0000    0.0000    1.0000
```

```
MTB > zinterval 99% 0.4768 for c2

THE ASSUMED SIGMA =0.477

                N      MEAN     STDEV   SE MEAN    99.0 PERCENT C.I.
C2            500    0.3480    0.4768    0.0213   (  0.2930,   0.4030)

MTB > let k1=sqrt(0.33*0.67)
MTB > print k1
K1       0.470213
MTB > ztest 0.33 k1 c2

TEST OF MU = 0.3300 VS MU N.E. 0.3300
THE ASSUMED SIGMA = 0.470

                N      MEAN     STDEV   SE MEAN         Z    P VALUE
C2            500    0.3480    0.4768    0.0210      0.86       0.39
```

Note: Since the p value = 0.39 > 0.01, the null hypothesis is tenable.

Problem 3:

Note: This problem can be treated as a one-large-sample test for the proportion of residents who would favor the Democrat. The null hypothesis is that the population proportion is equal to 50%. The z value for this test is

$$z = \frac{159/(159+174) - 1/2}{\text{sqrt}(0.5**2/(159+174))} = -0.82$$

At alpha = 0.05, the critical value is 1.96. Therefore the null hypothesis is tenable. We can also use the Minitab command ZTEST to do this problem.

Problem 4:

```
MTB > describe c1

                  N      MEAN    MEDIAN    TRMEAN     STDEV    SEMEAN
Method 1         36    208.00    207.43    208.14     48.92      8.15

                MIN       MAX        Q1        Q3
Method 1     114.12    301.92    160.93    247.26
```

```
MTB > zinterval 97% 48.92 for c1

THE ASSUMED SIGMA =48.9

              N      MEAN     STDEV   SE MEAN    97.0 PERCENT C.I.
Method 1     36    208.00     48.92      8.15  (  190.28,   225.72)

MTB > ztest 200 48.92 for c1

TEST OF MU = 200.000 VS MU N.E. 200.000
THE ASSUMED SIGMA = 48.9

              N      MEAN     STDEV    SE MEAN        Z    P VALUE
Method 1     36   208.002    48.923      8.153     0.98       0.33
```

Note: From the computer output, it is clear that the null hypothesis is tenable.

Problem 5:

```
MTB > dotplot c1 c2;
SUBC> same.

                            . .    :.::.   ::: :.::.. ... : :...   .
-------+---------+---------+---------+---------+---------Method 1
                                         .
                                       . :  .  .   .
               .           . .  .    :::..::.: .:.. ..    ..    .
-------+---------+---------+---------+---------+---------Method 2
              100       150       200       250       300    350

MTB > twosample 98% c1 c2;
SUBC> pooled.

TWOSAMPLE T FOR Method 1 VS Method 2
            N       MEAN      STDEV   SE MEAN
Method 1   36      208.0       48.9       8.2
Method 2   36      218.4       43.5       7.2

98 PCT CI FOR MU Method 1 - MU Method 2: (-36.4, 15.6)

TTEST MU Method 1 = MU Method 2 (VS NE): T= -0.95  P=0.34  DF=70

POOLED STDEV =       46.3
```

Note: This is a typical two-sided test for the difference between the population means. Since the p value is greater than 0.02, we retain the null hypothesis of equal means.

Problem 6:

```
MTB > set c1
DATA> 10.3 10.5 9.9 10.1 10.2 10.6 9.8 10.2 10.4 10.0
DATA> end

(a): MTB > tinterval 95% c1

              N      MEAN     STDEV   SE MEAN    95.0 PERCENT C.I.
Method 1     10   10.2000    0.2582    0.0816   ( 10.0152, 10.3848)

(b): MTB > zinterval 95% 0.2 c1

THE ASSUMED SIGMA =0.200

              N      MEAN     STDEV   SE MEAN    95.0 PERCENT C.I.
Method 1     10   10.2000    0.2582    0.0632   ( 10.0759, 10.3241)

MTB > ztest 10 0.2 c1

TEST OF MU = 10.0000 VS MU N.E. 10.0000
THE ASSUMED SIGMA = 0.200

              N      MEAN     STDEV    SE MEAN         Z    P VALUE
Method 1     10   10.2000    0.2582     0.0632      3.16     0.0016
```

Problem 7:

```
MTB > copy c2 c3 into c2 c3;
SUBC> use c3=1:4.

MTB > oneway data in c2, factors in c3

ANALYSIS OF VARIANCE ON INCOME
SOURCE      DF          SS          MS         F        p
SIZE         3        6694        2231     12.12    0.000
ERROR       82       15098         184
TOTAL       85       21792
                                 INDIVIDUAL 95 PCT CI'S FOR MEAN
                                 BASED ON POOLED STDEV
LEVEL        N       STDEV      ----------+---------+---------+------
    1       26       10.85       (----*----)
    2       21       15.29                  (-----*-----)
    3       25       14.55                          (----*-----)
    4       14       13.59                           (-------*------)
                                ----------+---------+---------+------

POOLED STDEV =       13.57              30        40        50
```

Note: This is a typical one-factor ANOVA problem. The null hypothesis is that the factor means are all equal. Since the p value is zero, we reject the null hypothesis, and we conclude that average per capita incomes differ among families of one to four people.

Problem 8:

```
MTB > read c1 c2
DATA> 45 31
DATA> 68 57
DATA> end
      2 ROWS READ

MTB > chisquare c1 c2

Expected counts are printed below observed counts

            FOOD    INCOME     Total
    1         45        31        76
           42.73     33.27

    2         68        57       125
           70.27     54.73

Total        113        88       201

ChiSq =    0.121 +   0.155 +
           0.074 +   0.094 = 0.444
df = 1
```

Note: At alpha=0.10, the critical value of a chi-square distribution with 1 degree of freedom is 2.706. Since 0.444 is less than 2.706, we retain the null hypothesis of independence.

Problem 9:

```
MTB > table c1 c2;
SUBC> mean of c3.

 ROWS: SCHOOL      COLUMNS: REGION

              1         2         3       ALL

   1     87.000    80.500    90.500    86.000
   2     80.500    74.250    84.750    79.833
 ALL     83.750    77.375    87.625    82.917

  CELL CONTENTS --
          ABILITY:MEAN
```

Note: From the above table of cell means, we cannot see any interaction between REGION and SCHOOL.

```
MTB > twoway data in c3, factors in c1 c2

ANALYSIS OF VARIANCE  ABILITY

SOURCE          DF        SS         MS
SCHOOL           1     228.2      228.2
REGION           2     428.6      214.3
INTERACTION      2       0.6        0.3
ERROR           18     390.5       21.7
TOTAL           23    1047.8
```

Note: The F statistic of the test for interaction is given by

$$F = 0.3/21.7 = 0.014$$

The numbers of degrees of freedom are 2 and 18. The p value can be found via Minitab commands:

```
   MTB > cdf 0.014 k1;
   SUBC> F 2 18.
   MTB > let k1=1-k1
   MTB > print k1
0.986
```

Since the p value is well above 0.20, we retain the null hypothesis of no interaction. That is, the differences in overall abilities of graduates from the two business schools are the same no matter which of the three regions we consider.

Problem 10:

Note: The F statistic of the test for the significance of SCHOOL is given by F=228.2/21.7=10.5, and the numbers of degrees of freedom are 1 and 18. The p value can be obtained by

```
   MTB > cdf 10.5 k1;
   SUBC> F 1 18.
   MTB > let k1=1-k1
   MTB > print k1
0.0045
```

Since the p value is less than 0.02, we reject the null hypothesis of no SCHOOL effects.

Similarly, the F statistic of the test for the significance of REGION is given by F=214.3/21.7=9.88, and the numbers of degrees of freedom are 2 and 18. The p value can be obtained by

```
MTB > cdf 9.88 k1;
SUBC> F 2 18.
MTB > let k1=1-k1
MTB > print k1
 0.00127
```

Since the p value is < 0.02, we reject the null hypothesis of no REGION effects.

Finally, the grand mean, SCHOOL effects and REGION effects can be obtained from the table of cell means. Precisely, the grand mean is 82.917, the REGION effects are

```
East:     83.750-82.917 = 0.833
Middle:   77.375-82.917 =-5.542
West:     87.625-82.917 = 4.708
```

and the SCHOOL effects are

```
School 1:  86.000-82.917 = 3.083
School 2:  79.833-82.917 =-3.084
```

Problem 11:

```
MTB > oneway data in c3, factor in c1

ANALYSIS OF VARIANCE ON ABILITY
SOURCE      DF         SS         MS         F        p
SCHOOL       1      228.2      228.2      6.12    0.022
ERROR       22      819.7       37.3
TOTAL       23     1047.8
```

Note: The p value of the test for the significance of SCHOOL effects is 0.022, which is larger than 0.02. Therefore, we would have obtained a different conclusion if we had analyzed the data as a one-factor ANOVA.

This file contains solutions to computer exercises in Chapter 9.
Filename: regress.ans

Problem 1:

```
MTB > plot c4 against c3

Consump -                                                         **
        -                                                       *
        -                                                  *  *
    2800+                                               * *
        -                                            * *
        -                                       *  *
        -                                      *
        -                                  **
    2400+                             *  *
        -                         *
        -                    *  *
        -                 *
        -              **
    2000+            2*
        -        * *
        -      *
        -
      --+---------+---------+---------+---------+---------+----GNP
       3000      3300      3600      3900      4200      4500
```

Note: Visually, we can see a strong indication of a linear relationship between consumption and GNP.

```
MTB > regress c4 on 1 predictor c3

The regression equation is
Consump = - 225 + 0.712 GNP

Predictor        Coef       Stdev    t-ratio        p
Constant      -224.69       39.43      -5.70    0.000
GNP           0.71194     0.01047      68.02    0.000

s = 28.29        R-sq = 99.4%     R-sq(adj) = 99.4%

Analysis of Variance

SOURCE       DF          SS          MS         F        p
Regression    1     3704269     3704269   4627.17    0.000
Error        26       20814         801
Total        27     3725083
```

```
Unusual Observations
Obs.      GNP   Consump        Fit Stdev.Fit  Residual    St.Resid
  8      3212   2117.00    2062.06      7.63     54.94       2.02R
```

R denotes an obs. with a large st. resid.

Note: At alpha=0.01, the regression coefficient is significant, because the p value for it is 0. On average, about 71 cents were spent in consumption for each additional dollar of GNP.

Problem 2:

Note: The sample coefficient of determination = 99.4%, which means that 99.4% of the total variation in the dependent variable is explained by the relationship between GNP and consumption expressed in the regression line.

Note: Test H0: the correlation between consumption and GNP is zero versus H1: the correlation is positive. The test statistic is given by:

t = sqrt(0.994)/sqrt(0.006/26) = 65.63

which is much larger than the corresponding critical value. So we reject the null hypothesis.

Problem 3:

```
MTB > brief 3
MTB > name c10 'st.resid' c11 'fits' c12 'residual'
MTB > regress c4 1 c3, store st.resid in c10, fits in c11;
SUBC> residuals into c12.

The regression equation is
Consump = - 225 + 0.712 GNP

Predictor        Coef        Stdev    t-ratio        p
Constant      -224.69        39.43      -5.70    0.000
GNP           0.71194      0.01047      68.02    0.000

s = 28.29       R-sq = 99.4%     R-sq(adj) = 99.4%

Analysis of Variance

SOURCE        DF          SS           MS         F        p
Regression     1     3704269      3704269   4627.17    0.000
Error         26       20814          801
Total         27     3725083
```

Obs.	GNP	Consump	Fit	Stdev.Fit	Residual	St.Resid
1	2978	1862.90	1895.47	9.54	-32.57	-1.22
2	3017	1896.40	1923.23	9.20	-26.83	-1.00
3	3099	1940.90	1981.61	8.52	-40.71	-1.51
4	3114	1960.20	1992.29	8.40	-32.09	-1.19
5	3112	1996.30	1990.86	8.41	5.44	0.20
6	3159	2023.80	2024.33	8.04	-0.53	-0.02
7	3179	2065.60	2038.56	7.88	27.04	0.99
8	3212	2117.00	2062.06	7.63	54.94	2.02R
9	3265	2146.60	2099.79	7.25	46.81	1.71
10	3367	2213.00	2172.41	6.57	40.59	1.47
11	3443	2262.80	2226.52	6.15	36.28	1.31
12	3545	2315.80	2299.13	5.70	16.67	0.60
13	3674	2361.10	2390.97	5.38	-29.87	-1.08
14	3754	2417.00	2447.93	5.35	-30.93	-1.11
15	3807	2450.30	2485.66	5.40	-35.36	-1.27
16	3851	2493.40	2516.99	5.49	-23.59	-0.85
17	3921	2549.90	2566.82	5.70	-16.92	-0.61
18	3973	2602.00	2603.84	5.91	-1.84	-0.07
19	4042	2665.40	2652.97	6.25	12.43	0.45
20	4104	2700.10	2697.11	6.61	2.99	0.11
21	4174	2737.90	2746.94	7.07	-9.04	-0.33
22	4211	2765.80	2773.29	7.33	-7.49	-0.27
23	4265	2837.10	2811.73	7.72	25.37	0.93
24	4288	2858.60	2828.10	7.90	30.50	1.12
25	4377	2893.80	2891.47	8.61	2.33	0.09
26	4445	2943.70	2939.88	9.18	3.82	0.14
27	4524	3011.30	2996.12	9.86	15.18	0.57
28	4607	3022.60	3055.21	10.60	-32.61	-1.24

R denotes an obs. with a large st. resid.

```
MTB > mplot c11 c3 c4 c3

         -
         -                                                     B2
         -                                                   2  A
         -                                              B  2
     2800+                                           2 2A
         -                                        2 2
         -                                   2  2
         -                                  2
         -                            A 22
     2400+                         2  B
         -                     2
         -               B  2
         -            B  A
         -         B2 A
     2000+      A42A
         -  A 2 B
         -  B

--+---------+---------+---------+---------+---------+----
          3000      3300      3600      3900      4200      4500

         A = fits vs. GNP          B = Consump vs. GNP
```

MTB > plot c12 c3

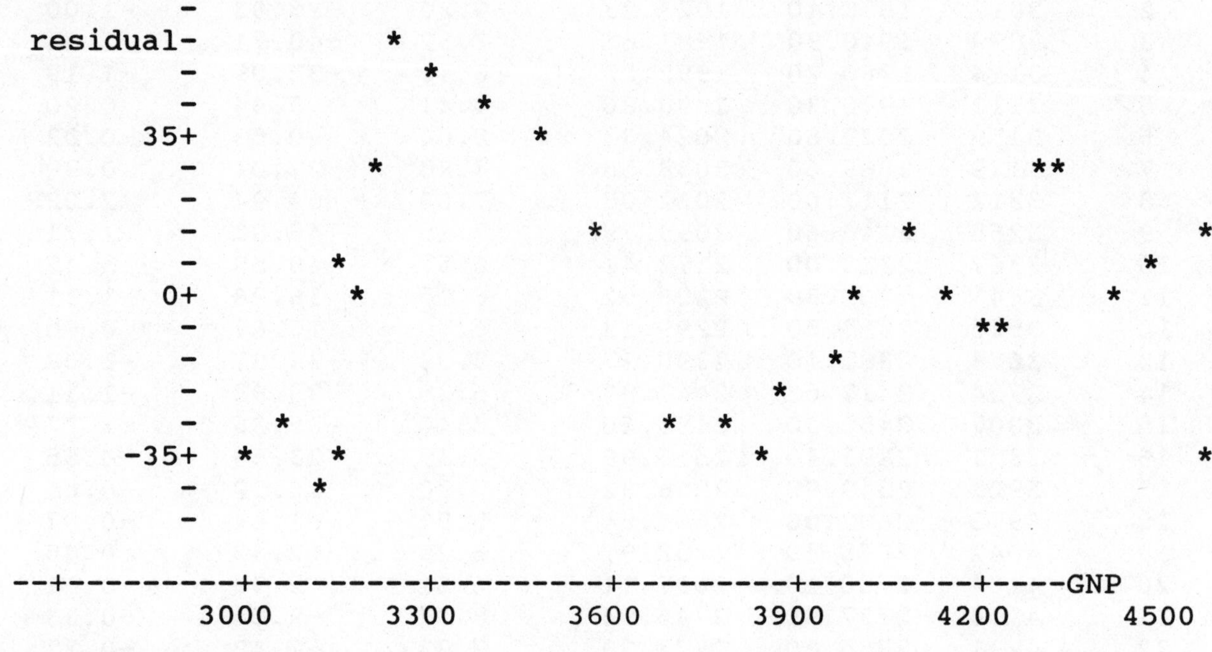

Problem 4:

```
MTB > let c20=c12/28.29
MTB > print c10 c20
```

ROW	st.resid	C20
1	-1.22248	-1.15112
2	-1.00279	-0.94842
3	-1.50880	-1.43902
4	-1.18761	-1.13429
5	0.20119	0.19212
6	-0.01939	-0.01860
7	0.99490	0.95564
8	2.01656	1.94207
9	1.71146	1.65460
10	1.47498	1.43481
11	1.31374	1.28255
12	0.60133	0.58910
13	-1.07549	-1.05600
14	-1.11324	-1.09330
15	-1.27325	-1.24998
16	-0.84980	-0.83377
17	-0.61064	-0.59820
18	-0.06664	-0.06518
19	0.45054	0.43946
20	0.10877	0.10577
21	-0.33009	-0.31967
22	-0.27389	-0.26458
23	0.93207	0.89679

```
24   1.12245   1.07796
25   0.08656   0.08247
26   0.14278   0.13508
27   0.57233   0.53652
28  -1.24319  -1.15279
```

Note: No residuals are more than 2s away from zero.

Problem 5:

Note: The test statistic is given by
t = (0.71194-0.7)/0.01047 = 1.14
The critical value for t-distribution with 26 degrees of freedom is 2.056, at alpha=0.05. So we retain the null hypothesis. The p value can be obtained by

```
MTB > cdf -1.14;
SUBC> t 26.
   -1.1400      0.1323
```

The p value=2*0.1323=0.2646, which means that by sampling chance alone, about one-fourth of the time we can get a 1.14 or larger t statistic, if the null hypothesis is true.

Problem 6:

```
MTB > plot c1 c2
SALARY  -
        -      *
        -      * *     *
     60+            *    * *
        -                *   *           *
        -             *        * *
        -          **   ****
        -                *   *   *  **
     50+           *                ***  2*   *   *
        -                        *   **    2  *2
        -                                ** *  *   *   *
        -                                *           * * *
        -                                      *        2 *
     40+                                       *    *   *
        -
        -                                         *      *
        -

+---------+---------+---------+---------+---------+------RATING
          0        20        40        60        80       100
```

```
MTB > regress c1 1 c2;
SUBC> residuals c10.
```

```
The regression equation is
SALARY = 60.4 - 0.198 RATING

Predictor        Coef       Stdev    t-ratio        p
Constant      60.3675      0.9602      62.87    0.000
RATING       -0.19801     0.01555     -12.74    0.000

s = 3.391       R-sq = 73.7%     R-sq(adj) = 73.2%

Analysis of Variance

SOURCE        DF          SS          MS         F         p
Regression     1      1865.9      1865.9    162.23     0.000
Error         58       667.1        11.5
Total         59      2533.0

Unusual Observations
Obs.  RATING     SALARY         Fit Stdev.Fit  Residual    St.Resid
 24       11     50.000      58.189     0.812    -8.189      -2.49R
 42       55     57.000      49.477     0.438     7.523       2.24R
 46       73     39.000      45.912     0.520    -6.912      -2.06R
 48       84     36.000      43.734     0.629    -7.734      -2.32R

R denotes an obs. with a large st. resid.

Note: Since the p values for the regression, CONSTANT and RATING
      are all equal to zero, we reject the null hypotheses.
```

Problem 7:

```
MTB > let c10=c10/3.391
MTB > print c10

C10
  1.12670  0.39375 -0.53470 -0.52025  0.98647 -0.02380 -1.52173
 -1.47192  0.79664 -0.61067 -0.13766  0.67106 -0.67492 -0.73624
  0.38203  0.07541 -0.62824  0.47265  1.17044 -0.79171  0.72360
 -0.41791  0.19806 -2.41501  1.02729  0.48417  0.04045  0.84918
 -0.63410  1.45655 -1.49388 -1.50122 -0.28081  0.01116 -0.23687
  0.72946 -0.83545  0.14552  1.64345  0.38496  1.11498  2.21860
  0.03752  0.32656 -0.07341 -2.03848 -0.24273 -2.28085  1.01264
  0.40839 -0.21070  1.90612 -0.22242 -1.35514  1.41280 -1.13621
  0.47851 -0.89092 -0.47923  0.71208

MTB > copy c1 c2 c3 c4;
SUBC> omit 24 42 46 48.
MTB > regress c3 1 c4;
SUBC> residuals into c10.
```

```
The regression equation is
C3 = 60.7 - 0.198 C4

Predictor        Coef        Stdev     t-ratio       p
Constant      60.6535       0.8274       73.31   0.000
C4           -0.19824      0.01340      -14.79   0.000

s = 2.827        R-sq = 80.2%      R-sq(adj) = 79.8%

Analysis of Variance

SOURCE        DF          SS          MS        F       p
Regression     1      1748.3      1748.3   218.72   0.000
Error         54       431.6         8.0
Total         55      2180.0

Unusual Observations
Obs.      C4       C3        Fit  Stdev.Fit   Residual    St.Resid
 48       85   50.000     43.803      0.553      6.197       2.24R

R denotes an obs. with a large st. resid.

MTB > let c10=c10/2.827
MTB > print c10

C10
  1.25077  0.37509 -0.74069  -0.71717  1.08566 -0.12511 -1.91862
 -1.86580  0.85975 -0.82946  -0.26225  0.71018 -0.90580 -0.97903
  0.36266 -0.00350 -0.84810   0.46697  1.30536 -1.04605  0.77409
 -0.60044  0.14297  1.13715   0.48738 -0.04877  0.92366 -0.85432
  1.64977 -0.68921 -1.89687  -0.43046 -0.07984 -0.38386  0.78031
 -1.10064  0.07906  1.87257   0.36577  1.23834 -0.05187  0.29565
 -0.18591 -0.39007  1.12161   0.39063 -0.34791  2.19213 -0.36034
 -1.72555  1.59518 -1.46059   0.47318 -1.16766 -0.67368  0.75368

MTB > copy c3 c4 c3 c4;
SUBC> omit 48.
MTB > regress c3 1 c4;
SUBC> residuals into c10.

The regression equation is
C3 = 60.8 - 0.203 C4

Predictor        Coef        Stdev     t-ratio       p
Constant      60.7778       0.7973       76.22   0.000
C4           -0.20260      0.01303      -15.55   0.000

s = 2.719        R-sq = 82.0%      R-sq(adj) = 81.7%
```

```
Analysis of Variance

SOURCE       DF         SS          MS         F        p
Regression    1     1788.2      1788.2    241.95    0.000
Error        53      391.7         7.4
Total        54     2179.9

Unusual Observations
Obs.       C4         C3         Fit Stdev.Fit  Residual    St.Resid
  8        12     53.000      58.347     0.662    -5.347     -2.03R

R denotes an obs. with a large st. resid.
MTB > let c10=c10/2.719
MTB > print c10

C10
  1.26437  0.42283 -0.77894 -0.63268  1.15361 -0.08441 -1.88505
 -1.96637  0.95399 -0.82476 -0.23822  0.81932 -0.88970 -0.95943
  0.44197  0.09332 -0.79605  0.46386  1.36280 -1.03873  0.90340
 -0.62992  0.23278  1.25683  0.61491 -0.01946  1.03807 -0.78649
  1.74494 -0.67573 -1.91854 -0.34419  0.02837 -0.41595  0.89383
 -1.13716  0.14870  1.94934  0.43718  1.28351 -0.01468  0.36267
 -0.17327 -0.40638  1.28075  0.39891 -0.28881 -0.26968 -1.81735
  1.64650 -1.49538  0.45429 -1.21646 -0.69965  0.75235
```

Problem 8:

```
MTB > regress c1 1 c2;
SUBC> predict 1.

The regression equation is
SALARY = 60.4 - 0.198 RATING

Predictor        Coef        Stdev    t-ratio        p
Constant      60.3675       0.9602      62.87    0.000
RATING       -0.19801      0.01555     -12.74    0.000

s = 3.391       R-sq = 73.7%      R-sq(adj) = 73.2%

Analysis of Variance

SOURCE       DF         SS          MS         F        p
Regression    1     1865.9      1865.9    162.23    0.000
Error        58      667.1        11.5
Total        59     2533.0

Unusual Observations
Obs.   RATING     SALARY         Fit Stdev.Fit  Residual    St.Resid
 24        11     50.000      58.189     0.812    -8.189     -2.49R
 42        55     57.000      49.477     0.438     7.523      2.24R
 46        73     39.000      45.912     0.520    -6.912     -2.06R
 48        84     36.000      43.734     0.629    -7.734     -2.32R
R denotes an obs. with a large st. resid.
```

```
   Fit  Stdev.Fit        95% C.I.           95% P.I.
 60.169     0.946   ( 58.275, 62.064)  ( 53.120, 67.219)
```

Note: The 95% prediction interval is (53.120, 67.219).

Problem 9:

```
MTB > regress c1 1 c2;
SUBC> predict 2;
SUBC> predict 3.

The regression equation is
SALARY = 60.4 - 0.198 RATING

Predictor       Coef        Stdev    t-ratio        p
Constant     60.3675       0.9602      62.87    0.000
RATING      -0.19801      0.01555     -12.74    0.000

s = 3.391       R-sq = 73.7%      R-sq(adj) = 73.2%

Analysis of Variance

SOURCE       DF          SS          MS         F        p
Regression    1      1865.9      1865.9    162.23    0.000
Error        58       667.1        11.5
Total        59      2533.0

Unusual Observations
Obs.  RATING    SALARY        Fit  Stdev.Fit  Residual   St.Resid
 24       11    50.000     58.189      0.812    -8.189     -2.49R
 42       55    57.000     49.477      0.438     7.523      2.24R
 46       73    39.000     45.912      0.520    -6.912     -2.06R
 48       84    36.000     43.734      0.629    -7.734     -2.32R

R denotes an obs. with a large st. resid.

   Fit  Stdev.Fit        95% C.I.           95% P.I.
 59.971     0.933   ( 58.104, 61.839)  ( 52.929, 67.014)

 59.773     0.919   ( 57.934, 61.613)  ( 52.738, 66.808)
```

Note: The 95% confidence interval for the population mean of all the second-ranking graduates is (58.104, 61.839). The 99% confidence interval for the population mean of all the third-ranking graduates is calculated by

(59.773 - 2.66*0.919 , 59.773 + 2.66*0.919), or (57.33, 62.22).

This file contains solutions to computer problems in Chapter 10.
Filename: multiple.ans

Problem 1:

```
MTB > regress c1 on 2 predictors c2 and c3

The regression equation is
Y = 69.3 - 0.0741 X + 14.1 R

Predictor        Coef          Stdev     t-ratio        p
Constant        69.35          24.73        2.80    0.009
X           -0.074137       0.007068      -10.49    0.000
R              14.122          2.348        6.01    0.000

s = 19.75      R-sq = 79.3%     R-sq(adj) = 77.8%

Analysis of Variance

SOURCE          DF          SS          MS          F        p
Regression       2       43257       21628      55.43    0.000
Error           29       11316         390
Total           31       54573

SOURCE          DF      SEQ SS
X                1       29143
R                1       14114

Unusual Observations
Obs.        X         Y        Fit Stdev.Fit  Residual   St.Resid
 21      3269     28.40     -21.69     4.01     50.09      2.59R
 26      3758    -65.30     -23.19     5.78    -42.11     -2.23R

R denotes an obs. with a large st. resid.
```

Note: The signs of the regression coefficients are not compatible with the theory. Since the p value is less than 0.05, we reject the null hypothesis.

Problem 2:

```
MTB > regress c4 on 2 predictors c3 and c2

The regression equation is
I = 90.8 - 7.29 R + 0.163 X

Predictor        Coef          Stdev     t-ratio        p
Constant        90.77          62.24        1.46    0.155
R              -7.295          5.911       -1.23    0.227
X             0.16262        0.01779        9.14    0.000

s = 49.73      R-sq = 77.2%     R-sq(adj) = 75.6%
```

Analysis of Variance

SOURCE	DF	SS	MS	F	p
Regression	2	242799	121400	49.10	0.000
Error	29	71707	2473		
Total	31	314507			

SOURCE	DF	SEQ SS
R	1	36228
X	1	206571

Unusual Observations

Obs.	R	I	Fit	Stdev.Fit	Residual	St.Resid
20	10.8	409.60	534.76	9.63	-125.16	-2.57R
21	10.7	425.00	544.17	10.09	-119.17	-2.45R

R denotes an obs. with a large st. resid.

Note: Since the p value for the slope coefficient for GNP is less than 0.01, we conclude that the slope coefficient is significant.

Problem 3:

```
MTB > let c10=lag(c2)-lag(lag(c2))
MTB > regress c4 on 1 predictor c10
```

The regression equation is
I = 475 + 0.746 C10

30 cases used 2 cases contain missing values

Predictor	Coef	Stdev	t-ratio	p
Constant	474.96	37.16	12.78	0.000
C10	0.7464	0.5137	1.45	0.157

s = 97.39 R-sq = 7.0% R-sq(adj) = 3.7%

Analysis of Variance

SOURCE	DF	SS	MS	F	p
Regression	1	20026	20026	2.11	0.157
Error	28	265559	9484		
Total	29	285585			

Unusual Observations

Obs.	C10	I	Fit	Stdev.Fit	Residual	St.Resid
26	141	673.3	580.6	43.8	92.7	1.07 X

X denotes an obs. whose X value gives it large influence.

Note: Since the p value for c10 is greater than 0.10, c10 is not significant. Investment Theory (I) gets more support.

Problem 4:

```
MTB > plot c1 versus c2

         -
IP       -                                                         ****
         -                                                      **
         -                                           *** * 2 2 2*2
     105+                                     ** * *        4  ***
         -                          **    * ***                *
         -                       ***** 32**
         -                    222*     2*
         -                 23 6*
      70+                *26
         -             *3*
         -            62
         -           +6
         -          +6
      35+        *57
         -       45
         -

--------+---------+---------+---------+---------+--------PXI
                 60       120       180       240       300
```

Note: A simple straight line would not fit the data very well.

```
MTB > set c3
DATA> 57(1) 93(0)
MTB > end

MTB > name c3 'DUMMY'

MTB > regress c1 on 2 predictors c2 and c3
```

The regression equation is
IP = 58.7 + 0.200 PXI - 24.3 DUMMY

Predictor	Coef	Stdev	t-ratio	p
Constant	58.662	1.270	46.18	0.000
PXI	0.200470	0.007196	27.86	0.000
DUMMY	-24.301	1.369	-17.75	0.000

s = 6.294   R-sq = 95.1%   R-sq(adj) = 95.1%

Analysis of Variance

SOURCE	DF	SS	MS	F	p
Regression	2	113853	56926	1436.89	0.000
Error	147	5824	40		
Total	149	119677			

SOURCE	DF	SEQ SS
PXI	1	101376
DUMMY	1	12477

Unusual Observations

Obs.	PXI	IP	Fit	Stdev.Fit	Residual	St.Resid
58	40	52.800	66.753	1.032	-13.953	-2.25R
59	41	53.367	66.903	1.028	-13.537	-2.18R
60	41	53.833	66.883	1.028	-13.050	-2.10R
138	288	103.700	116.406	1.180	-12.706	-2.06R
139	280	101.933	114.716	1.130	-12.782	-2.06R

R denotes an obs. with a large st. resid.

Note: The DUMMY variable is significant at any level. The introduction of DUMMY to the model implies a shift change from one period to another, perhaps due to increased productivity.

Problem 5:

MTB > correlation c1-c4

	U	CPI	E
CPI	-0.620		
E	-0.576	0.221	
I	-0.816	0.883	0.458

Note: As can be seen, there is a considerable amount of collinearity.

Problem 6:

MTB > regress c5 on 4 predictors c1-c4

The regression equation is
DOW = - 4157 + 9.1 U + 39.3 CPI + 0.0440 E + 0.0226 I

Predictor	Coef	Stdev	t-ratio	p
Constant	-4156.5	817.1	-5.09	0.000
U	9.13	35.79	0.26	0.799
CPI	39.278	8.139	4.83	0.000
E	0.04400	0.01820	2.42	0.018
I	0.02265	0.01591	1.42	0.158

s = 228.2   R-sq = 78.3%   R-sq(adj) = 77.2%

Analysis of Variance

SOURCE	DF	SS	MS	F	p
Regression	4	14815729	3703932	71.12	0.000
Error	79	4114254	52079		
Total	83	18929984			

SOURCE	DF	SEQ SS
U	1	8034677
CPI	1	6230210
E	1	445264
I	1	105577

Unusual Observations

Obs.	U	DOW	Fit	Stdev.Fit	Residual	St.Resid
80	5.7	2655.0	2056.3	49.0	598.7	2.69R
81	5.6	2570.8	2095.6	59.1	475.2	2.16R
84	5.4	1910.1	2319.0	101.7	-408.9	-2.00RX

R denotes an obs. with a large st. resid.
X denotes an obs. whose X value gives it large influence.

Note: c1 has the largest p value.

MTB > regress c5 3 c2-c4

The regression equation is
DOW = - 4050 + 39.8 CPI + 0.0427 E + 0.0202 I

Predictor	Coef	Stdev	t-ratio	p
Constant	-4050.4	698.9	-5.80	0.000
CPI	39.779	7.851	5.07	0.000
E	0.04271	0.01738	2.46	0.016
I	0.02022	0.01267	1.60	0.115

s = 226.9   R-sq = 78.2%   R-sq(adj) = 77.4%

Analysis of Variance

SOURCE	DF	SS	MS	F	p
Regression	3	14812342	4937448	95.93	0.000
Error	80	4117640	51471		
Total	83	18929982			

SOURCE	DF	SEQ SS
CPI	1	13808764
E	1	872545
I	1	131033

Unusual Observations

Obs.	CPI	DOW	Fit	Stdev.Fit	Residual	St.Resid
1	87	962.1	634.3	93.0	327.8	1.58 X
3	88	987.2	881.5	92.7	105.7	0.51 X
80	114	2655.0	2058.2	48.2	596.8	2.69R
81	115	2570.8	2099.5	56.7	471.3	2.15R
83	115	1931.9	2274.1	85.9	-342.2	-1.63 X
84	115	1910.1	2316.3	100.5	-406.2	-2.00 X

R denotes an obs. with a large st. resid.
X denotes an obs. whose X value gives it large influence.

Note: The p values of c2 to c4 change slightly after deleting c1. Note also that we have almost the same R-square, so c1 is really negligible.

Problem 7:

```
MTB > stepwise regress c5 on 4 predictors c1-c4

 STEPWISE REGRESSION OF   DOW    ON  4 PREDICTORS, WITH N =  84

     STEP          1         2
CONSTANT       -4216     -4977

CPI             54.2      51.1
T-RATIO        14.87     14.92

E                        0.059
T-RATIO                   4.08

S                250       229
R-SQ           72.95     77.56
```

Note: Select CPI and E.

Problem 8:

```
MTB > copy c1-c5 c1-c5;
SUBC> use 1:80.

MTB > regress c5 4 c1-c4

The regression equation is
DOW = - 5038 + 23.8 U + 42.5 CPI + 0.0705 E + 0.0211 I

Predictor          Coef          Stdev     t-ratio        p
Constant        -5038.4          880.5       -5.72    0.000
U                 23.76          34.44        0.69    0.493
CPI              42.493          8.098        5.25    0.000
E               0.07049        0.02090        3.37    0.001
I               0.02107        0.01548        1.36    0.178

s = 216.5        R-sq = 78.0%      R-sq(adj) = 76.9%

Analysis of Variance

SOURCE        DF           SS           MS          F         p
Regression     4     12502493      3125623      66.66     0.000
Error         75      3516706        46889
Total         79     16019199
```

SOURCE	DF	SEQ SS
U	1	5856832
CPI	1	5839887
E	1	718895
I	1	86880

Unusual Observations

Obs.	U	DOW	Fit	Stdev.Fit	Residual	St.Resid
3	7.6	987.2	968.3	95.4	18.9	0.10 X
73	7.2	2065.1	1618.0	59.6	447.2	2.15R
80	5.7	2655.0	2107.8	57.0	547.2	2.62R

R denotes an obs. with a large st. resid.
X denotes an obs. whose X value gives it large influence.

Note: The signs of the regression coefficients remain the same. The last 4 observations are influential, because they change the values of some coefficients and the p values quite a bit.

This file contains solutions to computer problems in Chapter 11.
Filename: series.ans

Problem 1:

```
MTB > tsplot c1
```

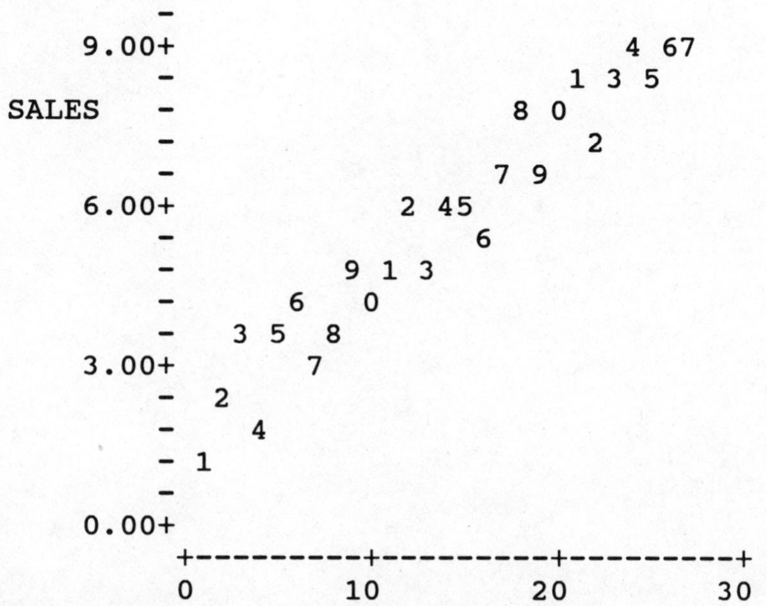

Note: Strictly speaking, one cannot observe a trend movement over a period as short as 27 months. However, a straight line does appear to fit the general upward movement of the 27 month periods.

Problem 2:

```
MTB > name c2 'TIME'
MTB > set c2
DATA> 1:27
MTB > end

MTB > regress c1 1 c2;
SUBC> residuals in c10.

The regression equation is
SALES = 1.81 + 0.278 TIME

Predictor        Coef       Stdev    t-ratio        p
Constant       1.8120      0.2397       7.56    0.000
TIME          0.27772     0.01496      18.56    0.000

s = 0.6055      R-sq = 93.2%     R-sq(adj) = 93.0%
```

Analysis of Variance

SOURCE	DF	SS	MS	F	p
Regression	1	126.33	126.33	344.55	0.000
Error	25	9.17	0.37		
Total	26	135.50			

```
MTB > name c10 'RESIDUAL'

MTB > plot c10 c2
```

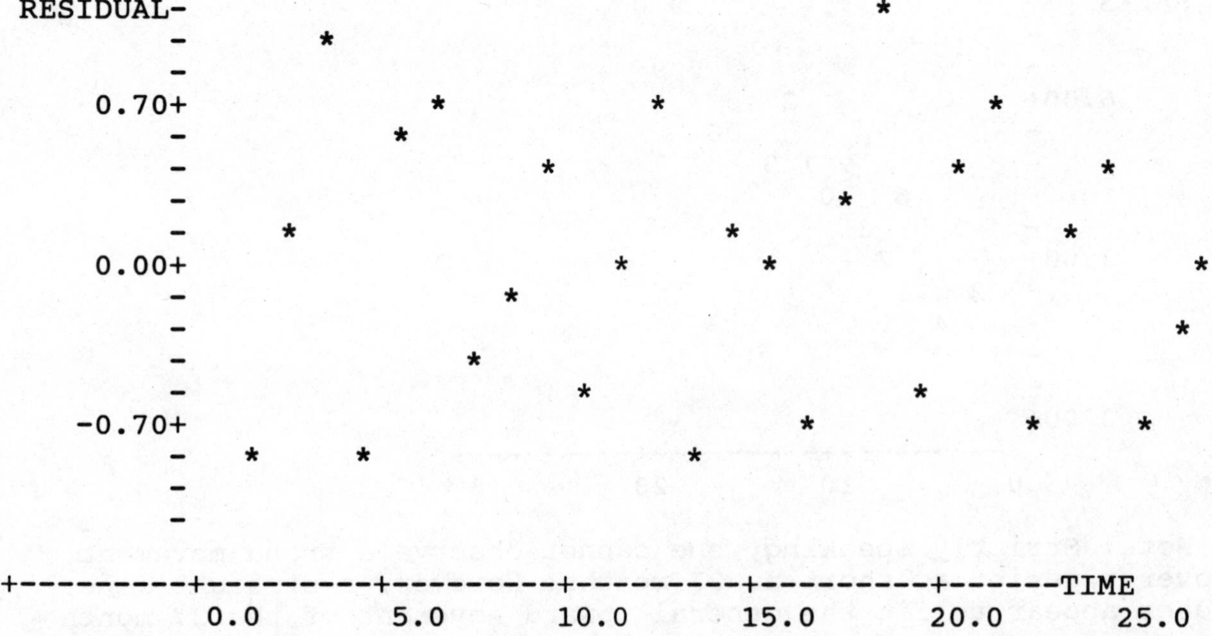

Note: As was true for the original data, there is no discernible evidence of cyclical fluctuations. Seasonal movements may be present. However, a longer time period would be required to settle such questions.

Problem 3:

MTB > acf c10

ACF of RESIDUAL

```
              -1.0 -0.8 -0.6 -0.4 -0.2  0.0  0.2  0.4  0.6  0.8  1.0
                +----+----+----+----+----+----+----+----+----+----+
   1  -0.351                   XXXXXXXXXX
   2  -0.389                  XXXXXXXXXXX
   3   0.699                             XXXXXXXXXXXXXXXXXX
   4  -0.347                   XXXXXXXXXX
   5  -0.395                  XXXXXXXXXXX
   6   0.562                             XXXXXXXXXXXXXXX
   7  -0.267                     XXXXXXXX
   8  -0.315                    XXXXXXXXX
   9   0.494                             XXXXXXXXXXXXX
  10  -0.274                     XXXXXXXX
  11  -0.196                       XXXXXX
  12   0.440                             XXXXXXXXXXXX
  13  -0.200                       XXXXXX
  14  -0.145                        XXXXX
  15   0.418                             XXXXXXXXXXX
```

MTB > lag 3 c1, put into c3

MTB > regress c1 2 c2 c3

The regression equation is
SALES = 1.15 + 0.0625 TIME + 0.750 C3

24 cases used 3 cases contain missing values

Predictor	Coef	Stdev	t-ratio	p
Constant	1.1460	0.2058	5.57	0.000
TIME	0.06253	0.03642	1.72	0.101
C3	0.7505	0.1213	6.19	0.000

s = 0.3543 R-sq = 97.3% R-sq(adj) = 97.0%

Analysis of Variance

SOURCE	DF	SS	MS	F	p
Regression	2	93.962	46.981	374.25	0.000
Error	21	2.636	0.126		
Total	23	96.598			

SOURCE	DF	SEQ SS
TIME	1	89.155
C3	1	4.807

```
Unusual Observations
Obs.     TIME      SALES          Fit Stdev.Fit  Residual    St.Resid
 18      18.0     7.9000     6.7743    0.0770    1.1257       3.25R

R denotes an obs. with a large st. resid.

Note: TIME is not significant, because its p value=0.101 > 0.05.

MTB > regress c1 1 c3;
SUBC> residuals in c11.

The regression equation is
SALES = 1.05 + 0.950 C3

24 cases used 3 cases contain missing values

Predictor        Coef       Stdev     t-ratio        p
Constant       1.0539      0.2073        5.08    0.000
C3            0.94993     0.03630       26.17    0.000

s = 0.3697      R-sq = 96.9%     R-sq(adj) = 96.7%

Analysis of Variance

SOURCE        DF          SS          MS         F         p
Regression     1      93.592      93.592    684.93     0.000
Error         22       3.006       0.137
Total         23      96.598

Unusual Observations
Obs.       C3      SALES          Fit Stdev.Fit  Residual    St.Resid
 18      6.00     7.9000     6.7535    0.0794    1.1465       3.18R

R denotes an obs. with a large st. resid.
```

```
MTB > plot c11 c2

     1.20+                                   *
         -
 C11     -
         -
         -
     0.60+
         -
         -
         -         *   *         *         *   * *         *
         -                     *     *   *
     0.00+                                           *
         -       *                                 *   * *
         -           *       *     *                         * *
         -                 *
         -
    -0.60+                             *
         -               *

--------+---------+---------+---------+---------+--------TIME
                     5.0      10.0      15.0      20.0      25.0

         N* = 3
```

Note: Visually, c11 does not show a clear cyclical movement.

Problem 4:

```
MTB > acf c11

ACF of C11

          -1.0 -0.8 -0.6 -0.4 -0.2  0.0  0.2  0.4  0.6  0.8  1.0
            +----+----+----+----+----+----+----+----+----+----+
  1   0.110                          XXXX
  2   0.211                          XXXXXX
  3  -0.384                XXXXXXXXXXX
  4  -0.104                       XXXX
  5  -0.039                         XX
  6   0.097                          XXX
  7   0.234                          XXXXXXX
  8  -0.233                    XXXXXXX
  9  -0.192                     XXXXXX
 10  -0.409                XXXXXXXXXXX
 11   0.075                          XXX
 12  -0.112                       XXXX
 13   0.169                          XXXXX
 14  -0.028                         XX
```

```
MTB > arima 3 0 0 c11

Estimates at each iteration
Iteration         SSE      Parameters
    0         3.29506     0.100      0.100      0.100      0.070
    1         2.79930     0.129      0.138     -0.050      0.048
    2         2.45222     0.156      0.176     -0.200      0.029
    3         2.24339     0.183      0.216     -0.350      0.012
    4         2.16624     0.203      0.260     -0.486      0.001
    5         2.16263     0.200      0.275     -0.510      0.001
    6         2.16232     0.198      0.280     -0.516      0.002
    7         2.16230     0.197      0.282     -0.518      0.002
    8         2.16229     0.197      0.282     -0.519      0.002
    9         2.16229     0.197      0.282     -0.519      0.002
   10         2.16229     0.197      0.282     -0.519      0.002
   11         2.16229     0.197      0.282     -0.519      0.002
Relative change in each estimate less than  0.0010

Final Estimates of Parameters
Type         Estimate      St. Dev.  t-ratio
AR   1         0.1971       0.1948      1.01
AR   2         0.2823       0.1905      1.48
AR   3        -0.5189       0.1975     -2.63
Constant      0.00169      0.06663      0.03
Mean          0.00163      0.06410

No. of obs.:  24
Residuals:    SS = 2.11924  (backforecasts excluded)
              MS = 0.10596  DF = 20

Modified Box-Pierce chisquare statistic
Lag                  12              24              36              48
Chisquare   16.2(DF= 9)       * (DF= *)       * (DF= *)       * (DF=*)

Note: The absolute value of the t-ratio for AR 3 exceeds the
      critical value at alpha=0.05, so c11 is autocorrelated.
```

Problem 5:

```
MTB > regress c1 1 c2;
SUBC> residuals in c10;
SUBC> dw.

The regression equation is
BUTTER = 38.1 + 0.652 PRICE

Predictor        Coef        Stdev     t-ratio        p
Constant       38.112        5.976        6.38    0.000
PRICE         0.65181      0.05249       12.42    0.000

s = 18.71       R-sq = 71.7%     R-sq(adj) = 71.2%
```

```
Analysis of Variance

SOURCE          DF          SS          MS         F        p
Regression       1       54015       54015    154.22    0.000
Error           61       21364         350
Total           62       75379

Unusual Observations
Obs.   PRICE     BUTTER        Fit  Stdev.Fit   Residual    St.Resid
 36      106      67.50     107.40       2.36     -39.90      -2.15R
 52       94     136.70      99.25       2.43      37.45       2.02R
 57      457     342.80     336.25      18.67       6.55       4.81RX
R denotes an obs. with a large st. resid.
X denotes an obs. whose X value gives it large influence.

Durbin-Watson statistic = 0.47

Note: Since the lower critical value for the Durbin-Watson test
      is about 1.57, and 0.47 < 1.57, we reject the hypothesis
      of no positive autocorrelation.

MTB > name c10 'RESIDUAL'

MTB > name c3 'TIME'
MTB > set c3
DATA> 1:63
MTB > end

MTB > plot c10 c3
```

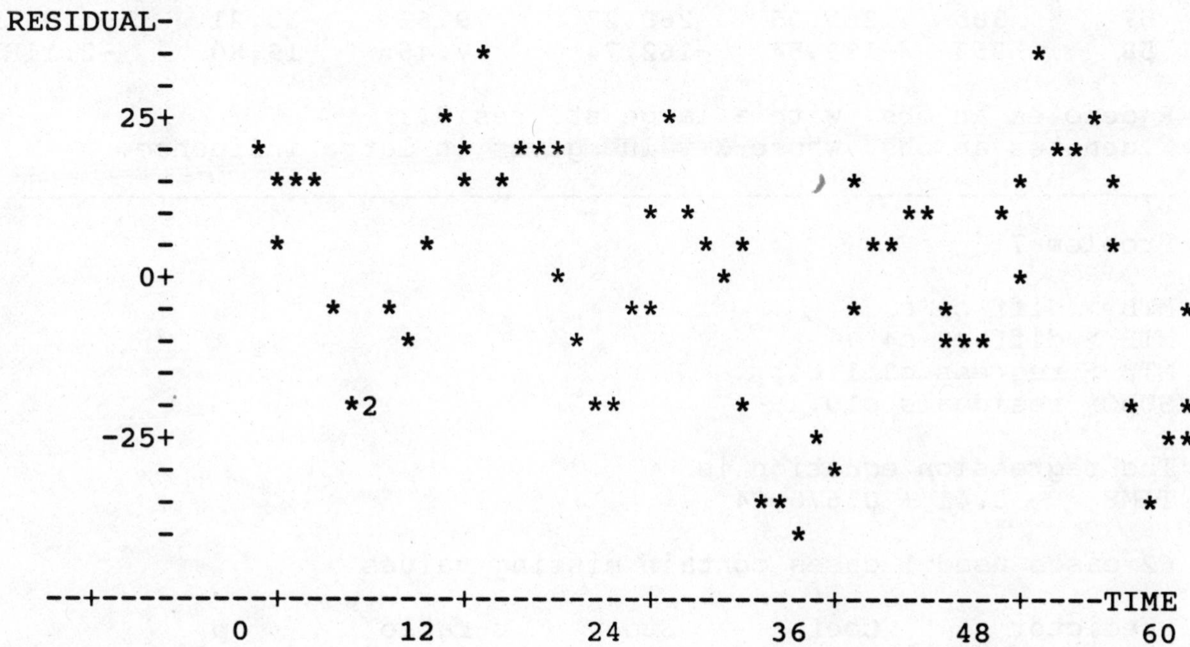

Problem 6:

```
MTB > let c3=c1-(1-0.235)*lag(c1)

MTB > let c4=c2-(1-0.235)*lag(c2)

MTB > regress c3 1 c4

The regression equation is
TIME = 7.99 + 0.675 C4

62 cases used 1 cases contain missing values

Predictor        Coef        Stdev    t-ratio       p
Constant        7.989        1.656       4.83   0.000
C4            0.67532      0.02633      25.65   0.000

s = 11.99       R-sq = 91.6%     R-sq(adj) = 91.5%

Analysis of Variance

SOURCE        DF          SS          MS         F        p
Regression     1       94641       94641    658.07    0.000
Error         60        8629         144
Total         61      103270

Unusual Observations
Obs.      C4       TIME        Fit Stdev.Fit  Residual    St.Resid
 33       26       1.40      25.29      1.52    -23.89      -2.01R
 52       20      48.42      21.58      1.53     26.84       2.26R
 57      385     255.05     268.27      9.62    -13.21      -1.84 X
 58     -253    -182.54    -162.74      7.46    -19.80      -2.11RX

R denotes an obs. with a large st. resid.
X denotes an obs. whose X value gives it large influence.
```

Problem 7:

```
MTB > diff c1 c3
MTB > diff c2 c4
MTB > regress c3 1 c4;
SUBC> residuals c10.

The regression equation is
TIME = - 0.41 + 0.676 C4

62 cases used 1 cases contain missing values

Predictor        Coef        Stdev    t-ratio       p
Constant       -0.405        1.628      -0.25   0.804
C4            0.67599      0.02504      26.99   0.000

s = 12.82       R-sq = 92.4%     R-sq(adj) = 92.3%
```

Analysis of Variance

SOURCE	DF	SS	MS	F	p
Regression	1	119770	119770	728.55	0.000
Error	60	9864	164		
Total	61	129634			

Unusual Observations

Obs.	C4	TIME	Fit	Stdev.Fit	Residual	St.Resid
57	363	228.10	245.18	9.24	-17.08	-1.92 X
58	-360	-263.10	-243.96	9.17	-19.14	-2.14RX

R denotes an obs. with a large st. resid.
X denotes an obs. whose X value gives it large influence.

MTB > acf c10

ACF of RESIDUAL

```
           -1.0 -0.8 -0.6 -0.4 -0.2  0.0  0.2  0.4  0.6  0.8  1.0
             +----+----+----+----+----+----+----+----+----+----+
  1   0.034                           XX
  2  -0.047                          XX
  3   0.195                           XXXXXX
  4  -0.138                        XXXX
  5  -0.161                       XXXXX
  6  -0.352                  XXXXXXXXXX
  7  -0.218                      XXXXXX
  8  -0.110                        XXXX
  9   0.073                           XXX
 10  -0.166                       XXXXX
 11   0.013                           X
 12   0.564                           XXXXXXXXXXXXXXX
 13  -0.013                           X
 14   0.008                           X
 15   0.202                           XXXXXX
 16  -0.023                          XX
 17  -0.098                         XXX
```

Note: The residuals are not strongly autocorrelated.

This file contains solutions to computer problems in Chapter 13.
Filename: nonpar.ans

Problem 1:

```
MTB > ttest 0 c1

TEST OF MU = 0.0000 VS MU N.E. 0.0000

               N      MEAN     STDEV   SE MEAN         T    P VALUE
LIFEINSU     100    0.0821    0.5648    0.0565      1.45       0.15

MTB > nscores of c1, put into c11
MTB > plot c1 versus c11

          -
     5.0+                                                          *
          -
LIFEINSU-
          -
          -
     2.5+
          -
          -                                                    *
          -                                                  *
          -
     0.0+              ***2*2323333434444444343333232*2****
          -          * **
          -
          -
          -   *
    -2.5+
--------+---------+---------+---------+---------+--------C11
           -2.0      -1.0       0.0       1.0       2.0
```

Note: Since the p value = 0.15 > 0.10, retain H0. The above plot suggests that c1 does not come from a normal distribution, and therefore the use of a t-test is, strictly speaking, not justified.

Problem 2:

```
MTB > stest 0 c1

SIGN TEST OF MEDIAN = 0.000000000 VERSUS  N.E.  0.000000000

               N  BELOW  EQUAL  ABOVE   P-VALUE      MEDIAN
LIFEINSU     100     28      0     72    0.0000      0.0521
```

```
MTB > sinterval 99% c1

SIGN CONFIDENCE INTERVAL FOR MEDIAN

                                      ACHIEVED
                  N    MEDIAN       CONFIDENCE       CONFIDENCE INTERVAL
POSITION
 LIFEINSU        100   0.05207        0.9876         ( 0.02856, 0.06804)
     38
                                      0.9900         ( 0.02800, 0.06819)
    NLI
                                      0.9931         ( 0.02679, 0.06852)
     37
```

Note: Since the p value = 0.0000 < 0.10, reject H0.

Problem 3:

```
MTB > wtest 0.05 c2

TEST OF MEDIAN = 0.05000 VERSUS MEDIAN N.E. 0.05000

                 N FOR   WILCOXON              ESTIMATED
            N    TEST   STATISTIC   P-VALUE      MEDIAN
AIRTRANS   24     24        38.0      0.001   -2.79E-04
MTB > winterval 95% c2

               ESTIMATED    ACHIEVED
            N     MEDIAN  CONFIDENCE  CONFIDENCE INTERVAL
AIRTRANS   24  -2.79E-04        95.0  (-0.02681, 0.02917)
```

Note: Since the p value = 0.001 < 0.01, reject H0.

Problem 4:

```
MTB > Mann-Whitney 98% for c2 and c3

Mann-Whitney Confidence Interval and Test

 AIRTRANS   N =  24      MEDIAN =          0.0140
 BROKERS    N =  35      MEDIAN =          0.0337
 POINT ESTIMATE FOR ETA1-ETA2 IS         -0.0389
 98.1  PCT C.I. FOR ETA1-ETA2 IS (   -0.0970,    0.0236)
 W =    621.0
 TEST OF ETA1 = ETA2  VS.  ETA1 N.E. ETA2 IS SIGNIFICANT AT
0.1285

 CANNOT REJECT AT ALPHA = 0.05
```

Note: Since the p value = 0.1285 > 0.10, retain H0.

Problem 5:

```
MTB > set c1
DATA> 27 35 30 33 26 37 28
MTB > end

MTB > set c2
DATA> 31 34 28 36 29 39 31 32
MTB > end

MTB > set c3
DATA> 25 29 32 32 28 38 33 29 30
MTB > end

MTB > stack c1-c3 c10;
SUBC> subscripts into c11.

MTB > Kruskal-Wallis for data in c10, indices in c11

LEVEL     NOBS     MEDIAN   AVE. RANK    Z VALUE
    1        7      30.00        11.4      -0.48
    2        8      31.50        14.6       1.04
    3        9      30.00        11.4      -0.57
OVERALL     24                   12.5

H = 1.084
H(ADJ. FOR TIES) = 1.091
```

Note: Number of degrees of freedom = 2. The critical value of a chisquare distribution at alpha=0.10 is 4.605 > 1.084, so we retain the null hypothesis.

```
MTB > aovoneway for samples c1 c2 c3

ANALYSIS OF VARIANCE
SOURCE      DF        SS         MS        F         p
FACTOR       2      16.5        8.2     0.56     0.579
ERROR       21     308.9       14.7
TOTAL       23     325.3
```

Note: Since the p value = 0.579 > 0.10, we retain the null hypothesis. This conclusion coincides with that obtained from the Kruskal-Wallis test.

Problem 6:

```
MTB > set c1
DATA> 2 2 0 1 1 2 0 0 0 2 1 1 2 2 0
MTB > end

MTB > runs c1

    C1

    K =      1.0667


    THE OBSERVED NO. OF RUNS =    8
    THE EXPECTED NO. OF RUNS =    8.2000
     6 OBSERVATIONS ABOVE K     9 BELOW
  * N SMALL--FOLLOWING APPROX. MAY BE INVALID
              THE TEST IS SIGNIFICANT AT  0.9108
              CANNOT REJECT AT ALPHA = 0.05
```

Problem 7:

```
MTB > random 20 c1;
SUBC> integers 0 and 1.

MTB > runs c1
    C1

    K =      0.5500

    THE OBSERVED NO. OF RUNS =  12
    THE EXPECTED NO. OF RUNS =  10.9000
    11 OBSERVATIONS ABOVE K     9 BELOW
              THE TEST IS SIGNIFICANT AT  0.6096
              CANNOT REJECT AT ALPHA = 0.10

MTB > stack c1 c1 c1 c1 c1 c2
MTB > runs c2
    C2

    K =      0.5500

    THE OBSERVED NO. OF RUNS =  60
    THE EXPECTED NO. OF RUNS =  50.5000
    55 OBSERVATIONS ABOVE K   45 BELOW
              THE TEST IS SIGNIFICANT AT  0.0540
              CAN REJECT AT ALPHA = 0.10
```

Note: It is more reasonable to reject c2 than c1, because the repetition of the five random sequences indroduces an element of nonrandomness.